Wings, Sun, and Stars

Wings, Sun, and Stars

THE STORY OF BIRD MIGRATION

written and illustrated by
JOHN KAUFMANN

William Morrow and Company New York

The author wishes to thank Dr. Helmuth Adler,
associated with the Department of Animal Behavior,
Museum of Natural History, New York City,
for reading the manuscript of this book.

BY THE SAME AUTHOR: *Fish Hawk*

Copyright © 1969 by John Kaufmann
All rights reserved. No part of this book may be reproduced or utilized in any
form or by any means, electronic or mechanical, including photocopying,
recording or by any information storage and retrieval system, without per-
mission in writing from the Publisher. Inquiries should be addressed to
William Morrow and Company, Inc., New York, N.Y. 10016.
Published simultaneously in Canada by George J. McLeod Limited, Toronto.
Printed in the United States of America.
Library of Congress Catalog Card Number 69-11849

For Millicent E. Selsam

Contents

Wings, Sun, and Stars

1 *What Is Bird Migration?*

A robin's song rings through the hush of an April dawn. Again and again the bold but mellow tones announce its arrival with the spring. Insects stir after winter, worms tunnel through the softened earth; the robin's food is ready. Each day the sun swings higher in the sky, warming the air more and more. By mid-May flying insects take wing. Swallows arrive on the warm south wind, dipping low over trees and fields. Noticing insect wings flashing in the early light, they turn, climb and dive, all the while gulping down their prey. Higher up, chimney swifts flicker through wide arcs of sky, seeming to follow the whim of their wings. Yet, like the swallows, they keep heading northward as they feed.

Along the shore a flock of sandpipers streak low across the waves. They wheel in a compact squadron, all alighting in the same instant to feed along the tide line. Yesterday no piper prints were on the sand. Today they have arrived, and tomorrow they will leave to resume their journey to the north.

That night the sky is clear. A tiny shape flits across the bright face of the full moon. Then another passes, and another. Twittering through the night, great waves of warblers and thrushes are traveling north again.

The robin has come from South Carolina, the swallows from Mexico, the swifts from Peru, the sandpipers from Argentina, the warblers and thrushes from Venezuela. By day and night, every spring, millions and millions of birds are on the move. They are traveling to nest and raise their young. Some fly many thousands of miles to the far North. Others, in the tropics, fly only a mile up a mountain. When their young have grown enough to take care of themselves, the birds return to their winter homes. Every year birds travel to and fro with the seasons in the movements that are called migration.

In both the North and South Temperate Zones, a regular cycle of four seasons is caused by changes in the amount and intensity of the sun's heat. During its yearly orbit around the sun, the earth tilts on its axis of rotation, causing either the northern or southern hemisphere to receive longer hours of more direct sunlight. When the northern hemisphere tilts toward the sun, spring and sum-

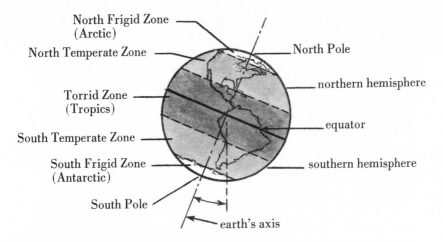

North Frigid Zone (Arctic)

North Temperate Zone

Torrid Zone (Tropics)

South Temperate Zone

South Frigid Zone (Antarctic)

South Pole

North Pole

northern hemisphere

equator

southern hemisphere

earth's axis

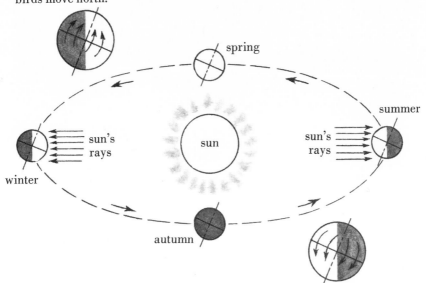

During northern spring and summer, birds move north.

spring

summer

sun's rays

sun

sun's rays

winter

autumn

During northern autumn and winter, birds move south.

The migrations of birds are linked to the seasons.

mer arrive. The days become warmer and longer, the nights shorter. At the same time, the southern hemisphere tilts away from the sun, so autumn and winter occur there, with colder, shorter days and longer nights. The reverse pattern takes place during the other half of the year. However, in the Torrid Zone, just above and below the equator, the sun's rays strike at a fairly constant angle throughout the year, and the length of day shows little change.

Many birds winter in the tropics, where temperatures are high and food is available. Each year the winter visitors crowd the land space and compete for food with birds that live in the tropics the year round. Before their nesting times in late spring and early summer up north, the migrant species leave the tropics, seeking more suitable regions to raise their young.

Most of these birds migrate north rather than south from their tropical wintering grounds. The main reason, most scientists believe, is that the northern hemisphere contains fifty times as much land area as the southern hemisphere, which is mostly ocean. In the North, a much larger area of land is available for nesting and feeding. Birds can spread out more widely, and thus the competition for land and food is reduced. The parent birds are then better able to hatch and raise their offspring, which is the ultimate aim of all migrations. In the Temperate and Frigid Zones, the majority of nesting birds must leave each year before winter comes and cuts off their food supply.

Sometimes individual birds of a migratory species fail to migrate. Each winter birds that are supposed to be wintering thousands of miles to the south are sighted in the North Temperate Zone. Among these stragglers is the whimbrel, a large sandpiper with a down-curved bill. Whimbrels normally winter in Central and South America, yet they have been observed at the end of December on Long Island, New York. Most stragglers die, but some of them find enough food in sheltered places to survive the northern winter. Man sometimes plays a part. Hardy migrants like robins and towhees may linger in the North all winter near well-stocked feeders.

whimbrel

black-bellied plover

There are also other exceptions to the typical migratory pattern. Young migrants that have made their first trip south often do not return north the following spring and may remain away from their breeding range for one or more years. Breeding is the basic reason for the yearly journey. Apparently immature birds that are sexually undeveloped and physically unprepared to breed do not have the full migratory impulse of adult birds. Black-bellied plovers, for example, usually nest within the Arctic Circle in July. One year, at the end of June, however, thirty of these birds were sighted on the Long Island shore, thousands of miles south of their nesting grounds. Doubtless they were immature birds that had not completed the journey from the South.

Among some species, only partial migration occurs. The geographic location—in short, the climate and food supply—and also the age and sex of the individual bird may determine whether or not it will migrate. Partial migrants usually make short flights, so that their breeding and wintering ranges often overlap. During the winter the migrant birds return from their breeding grounds in the northern part of the range and mingle with those birds that breed in the southern part. In the United States, certain song sparrows from the same brood in the same nest may migrate while the rest may be sedentary, that is, will breed and winter in the same place. The American goldfinch and the meadowlark are other partial migrants in this country.

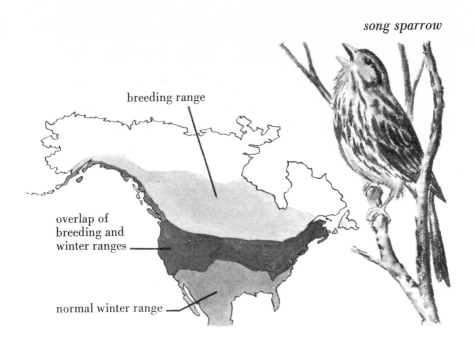

song sparrow

breeding range

overlap of
breeding and
winter ranges

normal winter range

In fact, whether a certain species migrates or not is often difficult to say absolutely. In Europe, starlings in different regions range from sedentary to fully migratory. In Scandinavia, female and immature chaffinches far outnumber males during the autumn migration. Most males remain in Sweden during the winter. Among other species, individual birds may winter in the North for two or three years, then migrate to the South the next.

There are also other kinds of bird movement, which should not be confused with migration. An irregular movement into a distant area, usually due to changes in the food supply, is called an invasion. The snowy owl, for example, is normally sedentary in the Canadian arctic. When its basic food, the mouselike lemming, suffers a sharp drop in numbers, however, the snowy owl moves south into the United States in search of other prey.

White-winged crossbills also make invasions. Using their twisted bill tips, crossbills pry between the scales of pinecones and spruce cones to reach the seeds inside. When they cannot find enough cones in the Canadian forests, white-winged crossbills fly south and invade the United States. Invasion differs from migration not only because of its irregularity, but because few birds making such flights manage to return to their breeding grounds.

snowy owl

normal winter range

invasion area

white-winged crossbills

invasions

Among other species, the young spread out and head in all directions after leaving the nest. Young seagulls and herons wander for two to five years before settling to nest, either on the original breeding grounds or elsewhere. This spreading out is called dispersal, and it accomplishes several things. First, it prevents overcrowding

19

and overcompetition for food in the breeding grounds. Furthermore, the weaker birds are unable to cope with the hardships of being on their own and do not reach maturity. Dispersal thus acts like a safety valve, reducing the pressure of overpopulation. Secondly, young birds are far more adventurous in their wanderings and may visit remote areas that the more sedentary adults never reach. Often they become the pioneers that extend the original nesting range into new regions. Dispersal is the main reason for the recent rapid spread of sea gulls along the East Coast of the United States.

Bird migration, however, is the most widespread movement of all. Each year, throughout the world, tens of billions of birds take wing to travel to and from their nesting grounds. Man still has much to learn about how and why these journeys take place.

2 *Feathered Flying Machines*

During migration birds fly for long hours, over jungles, mountains, plains and oceans. They fly on and on, their beating wings lifting and thrusting them forward. So very much smaller than man's great machines of flight, they nevertheless must contend with the same forces. Pilotless, except for their own instinct and experience, they travel by day and night, moving against ever-changing winds, beneath the sun and stars, through clouds and storms that catch them aloft. Pumping hearts and flexing muscles are their engines, driving the feathered propellers of their wings, burning their own body fat for fuel. Packed onto light, strong skeletons, fitted compactly within sleek, feathered forms often weighing less than an ounce, migrant birds are fully equipped, long-distance flying machines.

The physical performance of birds in flight is the subject of much study. Scientists have learned that while sedentary birds keep the same weight in early spring, migrant birds put on fat. When they are almost ready to start migrating, their bodies are plump and heavy. Then they fly. Although fat adds to the weight the bird must carry, it is the lightest possible fuel, giving twice as much energy for its weight as protein or carbohydrate, the two other forms of animal food energy. On their breeding grounds and in their winter quarters, migratory birds do not carry much extra weight. At those times, long flights are not necessary, and so their bodies do not store a great surplus of fat.

Replacing fat during migration is a fast operation. Human beings take some time to show the effects of eating a lot and put on weight slowly. During migration, however, birds can regain weight rapidly, thus cutting down on the time spent feeding en route. Many migrants must travel thousands of miles to reach their nesting grounds, so they do not have time for long stops to build up their supply of energy.

The longer the distance that the bird is about to travel, the more fat it will store up. One autumn night, large numbers of migrating songbirds were killed when they struck a television tower in Florida. They were examined to see how much fat they were carrying. The white-

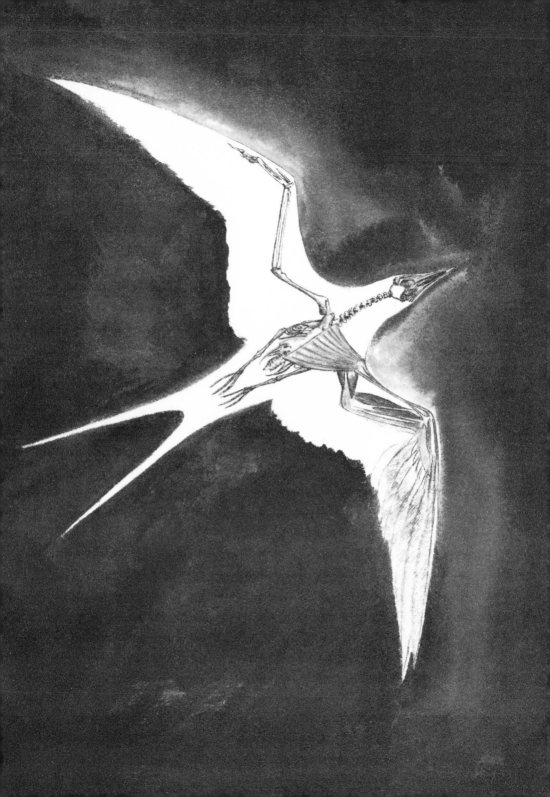

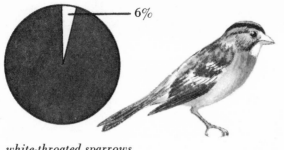

white-throated sparrows

various warblers

percentages of body fat in killed migrants

throated sparrows—medium-range migrants that travel from Canada to the southern United States—averaged about six percent of their body weight as fat. On the other hand, warblers, which migrate across the Gulf of Mexico to South America, averaged about thirty percent. The sparrows were near the end of their trip, while the warblers were still a long way from their destination.

Even people who know little about the scientific study of migration have noticed the large fat supply carried by long-distance fliers. The nearly extinct Eskimo curlew once traveled in great numbers between the Canadian arctic and South America. It was nicknamed "doughbird" by the New England gunners who slaughtered it, because when it was shot, its tightly stretched breast skin would burst on hitting the ground, splattering thick, rich fat. On the Caribbean Island of Jamaica, the bobolink is called "butterbird" for the same reason and is hunted as a seasonal delicacy by the natives.

To determine how these feathered flying machines perform, scientists observe the distance a bird can fly without

bobolink

Eskimo curlew

stopping to eat. The longest non-stop flights known are
made by American golden plovers. Each autumn they set
out southward from northwestern Alaska. Past the Aleutian Islands, down across the great sweeping expanse of
the Pacific, with no dot of land along the way, they fly on
and on. Their long, pointed wings, driven up and down
by strong flight muscles expanding and contracting, beat
three times every second, burning the fat the plovers
stored by eating insects. Hour after hour they push on at
about fifty miles per hour, through daylight and darkness,
riding tail winds and bucking head winds. Sixty hours
later, they reach the Hawaiian Islands 3000 miles to the
south. The distance they travel is amazing, but the small
amount of fuel they use is even more surprising. Starting
out with a total weight of about six ounces, they still
weigh about three and three-quarters ounces on arrival.
Man's airplanes do not begin to approach such high ef-
ficiency.

In general, larger migrants like golden plovers get
greater mileage from the fat they burn than do small
travelers like sparrows and warblers. Thus, plovers and
many other shorebirds can continue flying day and night
without stopping, covering a great distance in a single
hop. For very small migrants to make extremely long

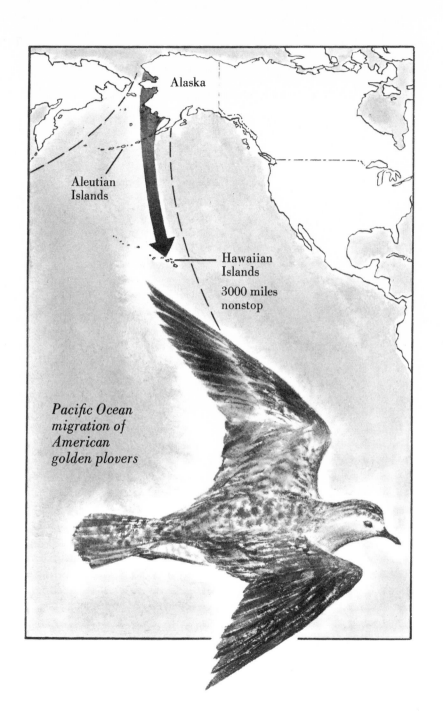

Alaska

Aleutian
Islands

Hawaiian
Islands

3000 miles
nonstop

*Pacific Ocean
migration of
American
golden plovers*

flights is unusual, but some of them do. The black-poll warbler, only four and one-half inches long, travels from as far as northwestern Alaska to winter in northern South America. Recoveries of birds that have been banded with identification numbers show that this warbler has flown 1800 miles non-stop from Massachusetts to Puerto Rico. Since it flies at about thirty miles per hour, this flight over the Atlantic must take sixty hours. The black-poll is such a small and seemingly delicate bird that this feat seems unbelievable despite scientific proof.

Each autumn slow-moving patterns, like dim "snow" on a poorly adjusted television set, appear at night on the screen of the radar used to study migration at Cape Cod, Massachusetts. Experienced observers know that these patterns are made by small songbirds, moving southeast in great numbers over the ocean at about thirty miles per hour. Since blackpolls are the warblers that store the greatest amount of fat before migration, and they are also the most abundant during migration through this region, they are the most likely species to be making the mass flights out over the sea. Furthermore, on the day following the radar sightings, ground observers in New England find a scarcity of black-poll warblers where they were abundant the day before.

Cape Cod
radar pattern

Cape Cod

Bermuda

1800
miles

Puerto
Rico

probable
main
route

Lesser
Antilles

South America

oceanic route of black-poll warblers

Blackpolls have arrived on the island of Bermuda two days after the radar sightings. However, too few touch Bermuda for it to be a regular stopping-off point. It is likely that most of the black-poll warblers continue southward until they reach the Lesser Antilles, 2000 miles away. Perhaps they even fly non-stop to the South American mainland, a distance of over 2400 miles. The final proof of this extremely long migration flight is still lacking, but all indications are that it takes place.

The ruby-throated hummingbird also makes a flight that for a creature its size might seem impossible. Each spring

ruby-throated hummingbird

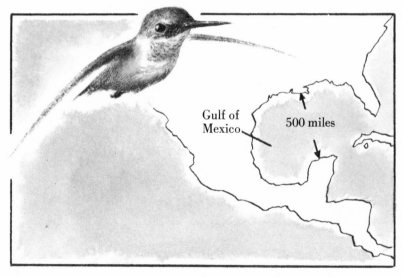

Gulf of Mexico

500 miles

and fall these three-inch shimmering red-and-green jewels of the bird world travel non-stop over 500 miles of the Gulf of Mexico between Texas and the Yucatán Peninsula in Mexico. Before leaving, they hover above flowers on blurred wings, probing for nectar that they convert into body fat equal to almost half their total weight. Then, like brilliant overgrown insects, they head out boldly over the open sea, flying at about fifty miles per hour, beating their wings at least forty times a second for ten hours without a pause. To make the crossing, they burn almost all their stored fat. These very long flights by little black-poll warblers and ruby-throated hummingbirds tax their energy reserves to the limit. Along with the American golden plover, they are the non-stop champions of the migrant birds.

An almost obvious fact about migration is that birds travel through the air. When they cover long distances, they do so by using their wings. Accordingly, the wings of those migrants that travel fastest and farthest all have a similar shape. They are long and narrow with pointed tips. In flapping flight, a long, narrow, pointed wing creates the greatest lift to support the bird and the greatest forward thrust to drive it through the air, using the least amount of muscular energy.

31

migratory

sedentary

Somalia
(sedentary
wheatears)

wing shapes

evolution of longer pointed wing in migratory wheatears

The wing shape of the wheatear, for example, is particularly interesting. This small bird migrates from Africa, north to Europe, west across the Atlantic to Greenland and Canada, and east across the Asian continent. The sedentary wheatears from African Somalia have blunt wings while migrant wheatears have evolved a wing shape closer to that of the other long-distance fliers. Their primary feathers, forming the tips, extend twice as far beyond their secondary or inner wing feathers as those of the sedentary wheatears. The difference might seem unimportant. However, their wings beat about twelve times each second for forty hours as they cross the ocean to Greenland. On such a long trip this small change in wing shape gains many extra miles for the same muscular effort. Thus the birds can better contend with the prevailing westerly winds, which act to hold them back and blow them off course.

How did the migrant wheatears get their wing shape? During the countless generations that they have flown over the Atlantic, natural selection has favored those birds that happened to have slightly longer wing tips. They were the ones that succeeded in completing the crossing, and thus they were more successful in breeding. Their offspring thrived. Eventually longer wing tips became a characteristic of all migrant wheatears, because the poorer fliers and their young were gradually eliminated. Among all species, the hardships of migration have acted over long periods of time as a harsh refining process, improving the flight performance of the birds.

Most migrant birds do not fly continuously, so their migration speed is hard to measure. They stop to feed, rest, and wait out bad weather along the way. The red-backed shrike of Europe, for example, flies at about thirty-one miles per hour, and its flight lasts ten hours during each night it travels. However, it does not fly two nights in a row. Instead of covering six hundred and twenty miles on two nights, it takes five days to go that far. Two nights are spent flying, three nights resting, and five days feeding. Its migration speed is thus not three hundred and ten miles per day, but a much slower pace of one hundred and twenty-four miles. Almost all species of birds migrate more slowly than would be possible if they pushed on as fast as they could. Thus their energy reserves do not run low, and they are ready for emergencies, such as strong winds over the sea or long cold spells, that they may meet en route.

Birds migrate faster in spring than in autumn. In spring the impulse to migrate is closely linked to the breeding urge, which speeds the birds along. Traveling at a steady pace, migrants stop just long enough to feed and rest. Then they take wing again without delay to reach their breeding areas with time to spare before actually mating. This time is spent in courtship and preparing the nest.

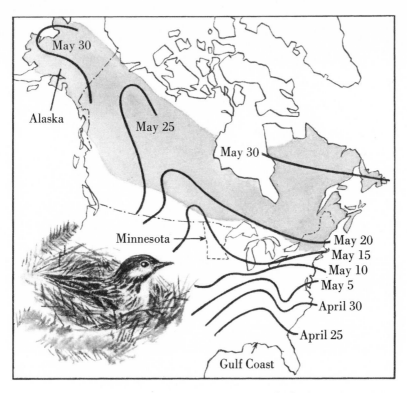

speedup in spring migration of black-poll warblers

Many long-range migrants speed up their flights as they approach their breeding grounds. For example, black-poll warblers traveling between South America and Alaska average between thirty to thirty-five miles per day from the southern United States to Minnesota. But from Minnesota to northwestern Alaska they average about two hundred miles a day. Once spring reaches the North, it comes with a rush and the birds can speed up accordingly.

Also, the blackpolls must hurry to cover the great distances to their nesting territories, which are as far as western Alaska, and still have enough time to mate and raise their young before starting back on the long southward flight.

Faster migration speeds in spring shorten the migration period of that season. The peak spring travel through the United States lasts only a month—from the end of April to the end of May. About mid-May great numbers of songbirds and shorebirds pass quickly by within a few days. At this time bird watchers sight more different species in one day than at any other time of year. In autumn, on the other hand, after breeding is over, most migrants are not in such a great hurry. They may stop off for days, feeding and resting along the way south. Although mid-September is a peak time, the busy part of autumn migration as a whole is more drawn out, lasting from July, when the first shorebirds return, to the beginning of October, when the last big flights of songbirds take place.

Flight speeds are hard to measure. Estimates made by ground observers show wide variations, depending upon local wind conditions and the bird's behavior when observed. A severe head wind can cut a bird's ground speed by more than ten miles per hour. A very strong tail wind

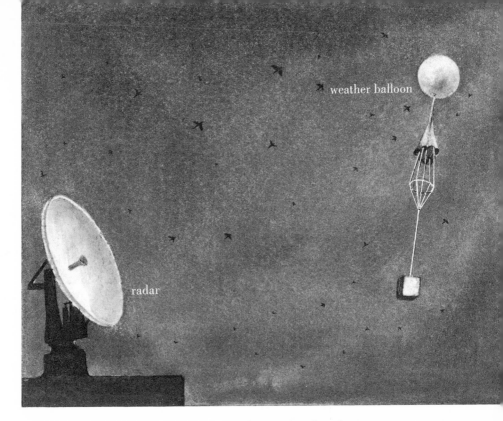

radar study of night migrants

can increase ground speed by the same amount. Furthermore, birds not only have a general cruising speed, they can put on a sudden burst to avoid dangers. For this reason, speed readings made by checking the speedometers of cars or planes running along with birds may not be accurate, for the birds may have been frightened.

Recently, in Illinois, radar studies were made during several migration seasons to establish the flight directions and speeds of birds moving by night. The radar tracks of the birds were compared to the directions and speeds of winds aloft, which were obtained by radio-equipped weather balloons carrying special instruments. The survey found that migrating birds choose the wind direction and speed most favorable to their direction of travel and flight speed. Songbirds, the slower fliers, favor winds below twelve miles per hour while fast fliers like shorebirds prefer stronger winds. Most birds migrate with tail winds whenever possible. In autumn, after breeding, birds will often delay their travels for several nights to find a favorable wind. In spring, on the other hand, the urge to reach their breeding grounds does not allow them to be so choosy, so they are more likely to fly against head winds then.

Scientists had always assumed that birds flapped at a fairly constant pace, regardless of whether they were fly-

Birds vary their efforts to keep steady ground speed.

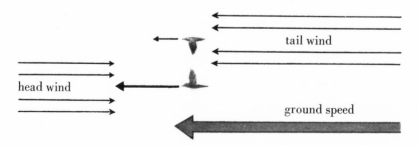

ing against a head wind or in front of a tail wind. However, the Illinois radar studies showed that birds vary their efforts. With a tail wind they flap more slowly. Against a head wind they flap harder. As a result, migrants maintain a fairly constant ground speed, despite changes in the wind, as long as its force does not become too great. Few birds can handle very high wind, so when it blows more than thirty-five or forty miles per hour, most migration stops.

A new technique developed to make direct flight studies of migrant birds is called airborne radio-telemetry. Now scientists follow the path of birds with radio receivers mounted in aircraft. The birds are equipped with tiny battery-powered radio transmitters, which broadcast a signal detectable up to twenty-five miles away. Night migrants, in particular, are being studied this way, for, unlike day fliers, they do not interrupt their flights. They fly continuously through the night until dawn.

Recently scientists in Illinois chose a night traveler, the gray-cheeked thrush, to follow. After netting it, they glued a dime-size transmitter to the thrush's back, so it would not hinder the bird in flight. Then they waited at a nearby airport, checking their plane, and hoping that the thrush would fly that night. Two helpers at ground receivers tuned to the thrush heard a wobbling signal sometime after dark. The thrush was taking off. Soon the plane was aloft, picking up the bird's signal as both flew northward toward Chicago. Fifty miles later, on the outskirts of the city, the scientists lost the signal in the strong car-ignition interference. But they held a steady course, hoping the thrush would do the same. Sure enough, they picked up the signal from the darkness on the shore of Lake Michigan. The thrush headed straight out over the big lake, but the human fliers could not risk a long over-water flight. They flew instead along the west shore of the lake.

Near 3 A.M. they were skirting a threatening thunderstorm by the north shore of Lake Michigan when the signal started up again. The small bird had traveled two hundred and fifty miles over the dark waters and reached the spot they had calculated just about on time. The thrush then flew north into the storm, so the human travelers had to give up the chase. At daybreak, forty minutes later, the bird would be over a large island where it could land. No doubt the men would have liked to follow it all the way. Still, tracking a small feathered creature for eight hours and four hundred miles during its migration was quite a feat in itself.

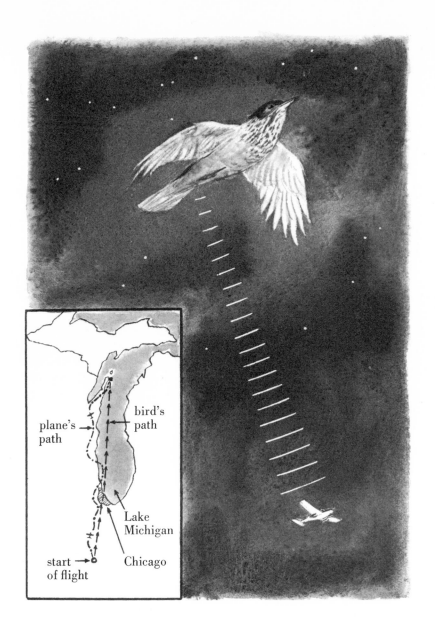

radio-tracking a thrush

The gray-cheeked thrush had held a remarkably constant ground speed of fifty miles per hour for eight hours. Winds aloft, checked by weather balloons, were also constant, possibly the main reason for the bird's even speed. They blew from the south-southwest at twenty-five miles per hour while the thrush flew at about thirty-three miles per hour, somewhat higher than ground observers had estimated for this species. This finding supported the claim of some scientists that birds fly faster during migration. Many further studies of this kind must be made in the future, so that we can get accurate information on speeds and many other factors of flight performance during migration.

Migration altitudes, like speeds, are also difficult to judge from the ground. Some of the most reliable earlier sightings have come from pilots flying at the same levels as the birds. Mountain climbers have observed birds flying on a level with their own height, and, most recently, special height-finder radar has given much accurate information.

Soaring birds ride upward on rising thermal currents from the heated land. They may be found circling at almost any altitude, from hundreds of feet where they first intercept a thermal, to thousands of feet, where they ap-

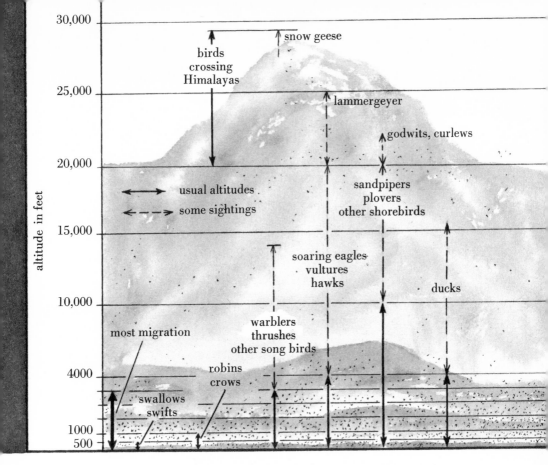

altitude sightings of some migrating species

pear as circling specks beneath puffy cumulus clouds. Migrating soarers, such as eagles, vultures, and certain hawks, do some flapping, but they prefer to use thermals whenever possible. Their flight is very efficient, since they derive their flight energy from the forces of the air.

Most birds migrate below 4000 feet, since they do not soar and would have to use extra muscular energy climbing to higher altitudes without gaining any advantage. Many day migrants stop to feed as they travel. Flying below 1000 feet allows robins, crows, blackbirds, and other species to observe food easily and to land quickly. Insect eaters that feed in the air, like the swallows and swifts, usually fly below 500 feet, where their winged food is most plentiful. On very windy days, wind force drops off sharply below 30 feet. Therefore, smaller birds fly as low as possible to save energy. Night migrants generally fly higher than day migrants, since poor visibility makes low-level night flying hazardous.

Strong, fast fliers like the shorebirds, which make long non-stop flights both day and night, often travel at high altitudes. Migrating shorebirds, such as plovers and sandpipers, have been seen quite a few times on the Cape Cod altitude radar at 20,000 feet and higher. Their flight headings, southeast in autumn and northwest in spring, show that they are probably going and coming on the Atlantic Ocean route to South America. They may be flying very high to gain maximum advantage from the prevailing winds, which are much stronger and steadier at high al-

titudes. Although songbirds are not strong fliers, they have been seen a number of times on radar at about 14,000 feet, so they too may be exploiting the prevailing winds at higher levels.

Birds, like men, are affected by the decreased levels of oxygen in air at high altitudes. Yet radar shows that birds travel as high as 20,000 feet, where the amount of oxygen in the air is one third of what it is at sea level. Climbers near Mount Everest, in the Himalayas, have sighted shorebirds like godwits and curlews flying *above* 20,000 feet. The Himalayas are the highest migration hurdle in the world, but a number of species, including seven kinds of ducks, regularly travel between central Russia and India, crossing through the snow-locked passes above 10,000 feet and even topping the great peaks.

The two highest migration altitudes ever recorded were those of birds crossing the Himalayas. A lammergeyer, or bearded vulture, was sighted at 25,000 feet by the British Mount Everest expedition of 1921. An even higher flight was recorded when an astronomer, photographing the sun through a telescope in India, happened to snap a picture of a flock of migrating snow geese. Calculations showed that the geese were flying at 29,500 feet, higher than the peak of Mount Everest itself.

The lammergeyer has a nine-foot wing span. It soars on thermals and winds deflected from mountains as it crosses the "roof of the world." This type of travel requires much less exertion than the steady flapping flight of snow geese, which must beat their wings once or twice every second in thin air containing only one quarter the oxygen of air at sea level. In one day's travel, showing no altitude sickness, snow geese ascend from the plains of Siberia, climb above altitudes where men need weeks to become acclimated, then descend to near sea level in India. Other species do the same. Without frequent breathing of oxygen, the human conquest of Mount Everest would have been impossible. Yet large numbers of birds, using only their hearts, muscles, and wings, perform comparatively greater feats every spring and fall.

Migration is the most severe test that birds encounter, a trial of endurance that strains their powers of flight, an obstacle course full of dangers. Not all the dangers are natural ones. When flying over land, night migrants may crash into buildings and television towers jutting up in the dark. One Wisconsin tower killed over 20,000 birds in a single night. Brightly lighted skyscrapers can dazzle birds on a misty night, causing them to hit the windows. The next morning, many migrants are found dead on the

lammergeyer

snow geese

sidewalks. For this reason, lights on New York City's Empire State Building and other very tall skyscrapers are turned down during the peak migration periods. Ceilometers—intense vertical beams of light used to measure the altitude of clouds for weather information—lure many small migrants into fatal dives. In Georgia a ceilometer killed about 50,000 migrants in one night.

However great the dangers of civilization may be to migrating birds, the forces of nature are a far greater threat. Over the sea at night, small birds are especially vulnerable. Very high winds can push them so far from land that large numbers fall exhausted and drown. Storms at sea can take an enormous toll.

One shipboard observer described the plight of small northbound birds, caught in a storm during their April migration over the Gulf of Mexico. Starting at noon the wind shifted from east to north, blowing at gale force. Few birds had been seen early in the day, but when the storm struck, large numbers suddenly appeared. They had been moving at higher altitudes, then had descended to seek the less powerful wind just above the waves. By four o'clock the gale was so strong that the birds could make no headway. In the calmer wave troughs they were fairly safe, able to hold their own, flapping to stay aloft.

But upon reaching a wave crest they were blown back
hundreds of yards into the sea and drowned. Some flew
onto the ship's deck, but the next crashing wave threw
them overboard. Many others were hurled into the ship
itself and fell stunned into the water. Still others sought
shelter by flying along the lee side of the ship. Whenever
they passed beyond the bow, however, they were blown

under. The observer was a naturalist, but he could not even guess how many birds were lost in this storm.

Unseasonable weather has caused the greatest known losses. One snowstorm in late March caught large flights of sparrowlike Lapland longspurs as they were heading through Iowa and Minnesota toward their arctic nesting grounds. At least 750,000 small snow-coated bodies covered the ice of two lakes alone. Altogether millions of longspurs must have perished.

To determine the annual losses of birds during migration is impossible. One educated guess puts it in the hundreds of millions. Nevertheless, more young birds must be raised every year, or the migrant species would disappear. This compensation depends very much upon the flight performance of the parent birds and whether they are able to reach their nests. Thus, the ability of migrants to overcome obstacles and to travel long and far on as little energy as possible often means the difference between life and death. Apparently bird travelers are equal to all the tests. More than enough manage to reach their far-off nests to mate and raise their offspring. Their species continue to change and to thrive, not in spite of, but because of the long, difficult, and hazardous journey of migration that they make.

3   *The Outer and the Inner Clock*

When the warmer days of spring come to the northern hemisphere, birds wing in from the South. The season advances, breaking the grasp of winter, melting the iced lakes, thawing the frozen ground, stirring new life in insect grubs burrowed in tree bark or buried in the mud of the shores. When crawling insects emerge on budding branches, warblers and thrushes arrive. When flying insects rise up on the newly warmed air, swallows and swifts appear. When still other insects peek out or skitter along the mud, sandpipers turn up, probing and darting after them. When flowers open, hummingbirds soon hover over them on blurred wings, sipping nectar.

Migrating birds are dependent on the climate and food supply they find upon reaching their breeding grounds after long, hard journeys. They must set up nests, mate, lay eggs, and raise their young, all in a limited time, before starting south again. Therefore, they must arrive in the North and depart for the South on schedule. During the many thousands of years that birds have been migrating, they have evolved flight schedules that bring them to their breeding grounds when the climate is warm, the days are long, and food is plentiful.

Climate change is most often indicated by the changing length of day throughout the year. In late winter and early spring, days grow longer and nights become shorter. On June 21, in the northern hemisphere, the sun reaches its northernmost position. It is the summer solstice, when daylight lasts longer than at any other time of the year.

Climate change is indicated by changing length of day.

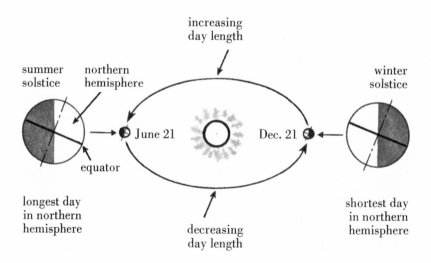

Afterward, the days become shorter and the nights longer, until, on December 21, the winter solstice occurs. Then the sun is at its southernmost point, and the northern hemisphere has its longest night of the year. This cycle is the outer clock, the clock of the seasons. It has no hands or numbers, but the periods of light and dark it brings, year after year, as the earth sweeps through its orbit, appear with a far greater accuracy and dependability than the time provided by any mechanical timepiece.

The northward movement of spring, with which birds coordinate their migrations, is a general climate change. Climate refers to the overall seasonal conditions of a region and not the daily change in weather. For example, average temperatures and rainfall during April in New York City are usually similar over a period of years. The day-to-day variations in temperature, rainfall, wind, and sunshine, however, show much greater change. Even though one April may be similar to another in terms of average climate, weather changes can be very abrupt. A sudden, late cold front, moving south from Canada, can drop temperatures sharply overnight. Accordingly, birds do not begin to migrate on the first warm day of spring. They wait to fly until the temperature remains above a certain level, a very good indicator of climate change.

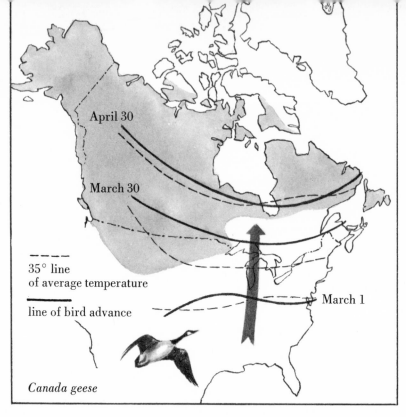

Weather migrants advance with temperature change.

Canada geese appear to fly with an average temperature line of thirty-five degrees. When sightings of these birds on March 1 are mapped, the thirty-five-degree line across the country marks the northern limits of their travels on that date. As the climate changes, the geese move north, traveling very close behind the tail of winter. At thirty-five degrees, three degrees above freezing, winter ice and snow are melting, and the geese are able to feed on the reopened lakes and bays. Robins also follow the same temperature line. Then the ground is thawing, and they can find worms and insect larvae to eat.

Birds that travel close behind the gradual advance of spring, and along with the southward advance of autumn, are called weather migrants. Unseasonably warm or cold weather may speed up or slow down their journey by as much as a few weeks from one year to the next. If it turns cold during spring migration, weather migrants slow down or stop moving until temperatures rise. If very severe cold occurs, they even may turn around and retreat southward, in what is called a reverse migration, until the weather improves.

Other species of birds follow the yearly clock of the seasons in a different way. Instead of advancing gradually with the spring, they lag behind in the South until spring approaches their northern nesting grounds. Then they make long, fast flights to catch up with spring. Their movements depend little on day-to-day weather, because they cover so much ground so quickly that they cannot know in advance what the weather along their route will be. Their arrival time in the North differs little from year to year, often despite unseasonable weather en route. Such birds sometimes are called instinct migrants, since they depend heavily upon their inner sense of time.

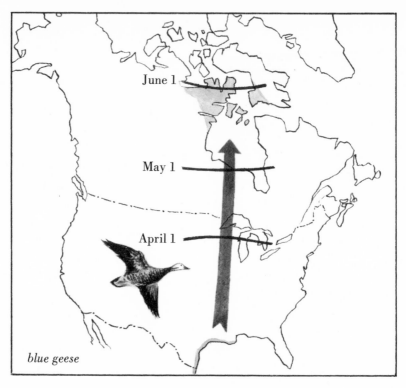

blue geese

Instinct migrants rely mainly upon inner timing.

Blue geese are instinct migrants, and they travel quite differently from the way Canada geese travel. They delay their spring flights a full month past the time when warm weather comes to their Louisiana winter quarters in early March. By then their breeding grounds near northern Hudson Bay, Canada, are free of winter cold. At last they take off in great flocks to make what may be a non-stop flight across 1700 miles.

Instinct migrants are very punctual. Although slender-billed shearwaters travel a looping course around the entire North Pacific Ocean, they manage to return to their Australian and New Zealand nesting grounds within the same eleven days each year. However, the promptness of migration timing is sometimes exaggerated. Cold, winds, rain, and food scarcity cause some variation in the yearly arrival dates. Popular legend claims that the famous cliff swallows reach the mission of San Juan Capistrano in southern California on the same day every spring. Such is not the case, although they do arrive the same week

slender-billed
shearwaters

cliff swallows

each year. Still, bearing in mind the difficulties of migration, this fact is just as amazing.

Almost all warblers, thrushes, swallows, sandpipers, and plovers are instinct migrants, arriving late in the North. Unlike most weather migrants, which eat grasses, seeds, or berries, these birds feed almost entirely upon insects. By arriving late, they allow insects time to become active and plentiful, and they avoid the highly uncertain weather of early spring, when sudden cold could quickly wipe out their food. Even though they arrive in the North late, however, these birds sometimes encounter cold waves, to which the smallest of them are especially vulnerable. Unlike weather migrants, few instinct migrants are able to retreat southward. The tiny warblers, which must feed often, suffer great losses if their food suddenly disappears. They lie motionless, strewn on the ground, victims of late cold.

Late spring cold spells do not occur very often. If they did, the yearly loss of small instinct migrants could lead to their extinction or force them to delay their migration even later. Normally the weather is warm and insects are out crawling and flying when they arrive. Some of the most flourishing bird species are instinct migrants, so their migratory pattern must be a good way to travel.

The outer clock of migration also consists of the daily cycle of light and dark. This cycle sets a daily activity schedule for migrant birds, and it divides bird travelers into two main groups: day migrants and night migrants.

At dawn the day migrants begin to stir. If they have not flown very far the day before, and so do not need to rest and feed to restore their body fat, they probably will start flying in the early morning. The pace of their flying depends upon the particular species. Robins, crows, wax-

day and night migrants

robin

yellow warbler

wings, finches, and herons, among others, usually do not make long, non-stop flights. They stop now and then to feed and rest. Swallows and swifts usually fly continuously at a leisurely pace, feeding aloft on insects. On the days that they rest, during bad weather or before a long overwater flight, swallows may remain near a favorite, traditional roosting place, making short feeding flights nearby.

Sandpipers, plovers, and other shorebirds, when well fattened and rested, may fly without stopping from early morning until late afternoon. If they are crossing a large body of water, with no stopping place, they will keep going after dark and fly by night. Extremely long non-stop flights, such as the 3000-mile trip of the American golden plover, may require several days and nights of flying until land is seen again. Such birds might well be called day-and-night migrants. Unless forced by circumstances, however, they usually fly only by day. Still, in early spring or late summer, one may hear the strong, sharp flight calls of shorebirds far above in the dark.

In fact, during migration, the night sky is alive with birds. About ninety percent of all migration occurs after dark. At that time the great migration waves, millions of warblers, sparrows, thrushes, orioles, wrens, vireos, fly-

catchers, and others, are aloft. When the moon is full, an observer may see small, dark shapes winging across its bright round face. Some scientists point telescopes at the moon to count the birds that pass. Veteran bird watchers can tell warblers from thrushes or shorebirds by their shape and motion in flight. Some experts can identify different species that look alike in flight, such as two kinds of thrushes or sandpipers, by picking out the individual flight calls. Special sound detectors are used to listen to calls of birds at higher altitudes. Radar picks up flight movements, and the tracking patterns are filmed to be studied later.

At dusk, night migrants as well as day migrants rest. However, day fliers continue resting throughout the night, while night fliers rouse themselves after an hour or two and take off. Night migrants must continue flying until dawn, when there is enough light to make a safe landing. Trying to perch on a branch or twig in total blackness could easily cause fatal injuries. When morning comes, these birds do not hide and go to sleep. They continue moving slowly along their migration routes, feeding and resting in between short flights. As a result, one often sees warblers and other night travelers during migration, as they flit through the trees in the daytime. Birds that

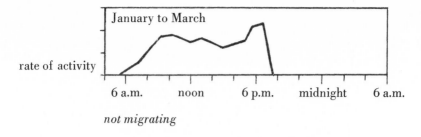

not migrating

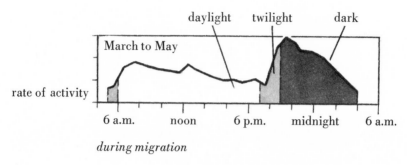

during migration

*seasonal monthly activity
of the whitethroat, a European warbler*

migrate at night are not normally night creatures. They are daytime birds, except during migration, when night flying is added on to their regular daily activity, like a kind of seasonal overtime.

Why so many species of birds migrate at night, when they can see more easily in daylight, is puzzling. One reason is that daytime visibility is not always an advantage. Small birds migrating by day usually hesitate when they reach a coastline. They are reluctant to start out across open water when they cannot see the other side. At night, small birds fly without regard for coastlines, or other unfavorable terrain, and cross even large bodies of water with no delay. In this case, what they do not see does not bother them.

Flying at night is easier work. During the day, the sun heats the land, causing local winds that birds must overcome. Also, the rising thermal currents that are such a help to soaring migrants are a hindrance to small flapping fliers, since they create turbulence in the air. In the daytime, small birds must use extra energy flying against sudden wind shifts and bumpy air. At night, local wind disturbances and the rising, rough currents quiet down, and the air becomes smoother.

Even more important are the long distances that many species must travel at a fast pace. Warblers and thrushes, among others, migrate to the United States and Canada from Central and South America. Because they are instinct migrants, they leave late in the spring. Once they depart, they must move swiftly. Night flying enables them to spend long, uninterrupted hours aloft, and they continue traveling, though at a slower pace, during the day. Without long, non-stop night flights, and day flights as well, they could never reach their distant northern regions on time. Unlike day migrants, they are not forced to rest for nine or ten hours out of twenty-four, so they can make almost constant progress. Small day migrants, limited to traveling by daylight, interrupted by feeding stops, distracted by the terrain, would never be able to travel so far so fast. Most of the instinct migrants are night travelers or can fly both during the night and during the day.

Although the outer clock, consisting of the seasonal and daily cycle of the earth's movements, has a clear effect on bird migration, it still does not explain what starts birds moving in the first place. For many years it was thought that when birds felt the warmer temperatures of spring, they started to fly north. We know now that the timing of migrations is not so simple. Robins, for example, do not start north too early if an unseasonable warm spell in January should occur. Warblers, in the hot jungles near the equator, where temperatures are almost constant, still fly north at the right time to reach their nesting grounds, thousands of miles away, when conditions there are best for breeding. Both robins and warblers need a more reliable indicator of migration time than temperature. Hunger is not the cause of their departure, since plenty of food is available in their wintering grounds when they leave.

dowitchers

There are many examples of migration timing that cannot be explained either by temperature change or food supply. In the New York area, each July, thousands of dowitchers, plump shorebirds with long, straight bills that probe the mud, can be seen resting and feeding on their way south. The insects and crustaceans on which they feed are abundant through September, but by August the great flights of dowitchers have already passed, flying as far as Brazil and Peru. Dowitchers start their return flight at the height of the northern summer, abandoning regions of plentiful food and increasing temperatures in northern Canada. How are these flights timed?

Scientists now believe that birds have some kind of inner clock that sets migration in motion. Just as the earth has its cycle of seasons, birds have their own inner cycle of activity through the year. Before they migrate to breeding regions, most species molt, losing their drab winter plumage and growing a new set of feathers. Males appear in the bright patterns of their courtship dress. As spring migration begins the sex glands of birds

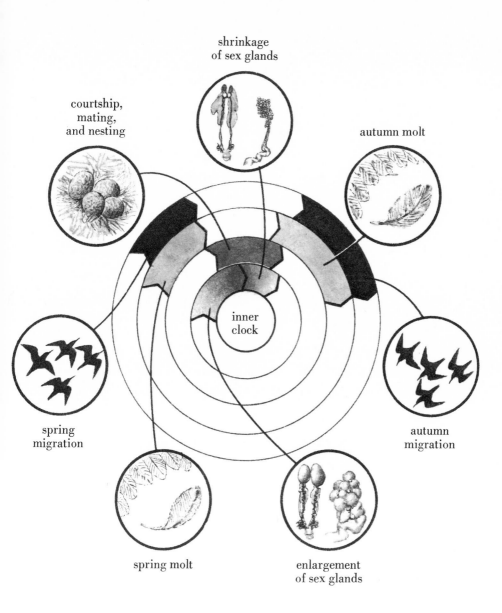

shrinkage
of sex glands

courtship,
mating,
and nesting

autumn molt

inner
clock

spring
migration

autumn
migration

spring molt

enlargement
of sex glands

*Migration is one part of a yearly cycle
controlled by the inner clock.*

start to enlarge. At the breeding grounds, the male testes and female ovaries reach full size, and mating takes place. Then the glands shrink, and, after the young can fly and feed themselves, the parent birds molt again, the males returning to their dull winter plumage. All these events—migration, mating, and molting—are timed and controlled by inner body processes in step with seasonal changes in the outer world.

Over many thousands of years, countless flights were made by the ancestors of present-day birds. Those individual birds that managed to fly to other areas at a time when the climate was suitable and food as well as nesting sites and materials were available bred successfully and raised many young. The other birds that arrived in the North too early, or failed to find suitable breeding grounds, did not survive to raise any young. Through many generations, those birds whose timing was in step with the seasons gradually displaced those whose timing was not. Thus, what began as hit-or-miss movements became, through natural selection, reliable yearly timetables for each species, passed on from parents to young through the genes as inherited patterns.

Slowly the inner cycle of birds has become adapted to natural conditions in their winter home, along their route of travel, and in their breeding grounds. One of the most important conditions is the increasing or decreasing length of day and night, which corresponds to certain times of the year, and these changes have a great effect on birds. For example, when the amount of daylight in Florida increases in late winter and early spring, the inner processes of a sparrow wintering there prepare it for migration and mating.

Many experiments have been made showing the direct relationship between increasing day length and readiness to breed and migrate. One of the earliest was conducted by William Rowan, a biologist at the University of Alberta in Canada. Dr. Rowan held captive slate-colored juncos, which normally migrate from central Canada to the United States in the fall, after the rest of their fellows flew south. Using one group as a control, he exposed the birds to the number of daylight hours natural to the area for that time of year. Another group he exposed to artificially lengthened days by turning on

slate-colored junco

electric lights in their cage after dark. Before long the juncos in the lighted cage were ready to breed. They fluttered restlessly, and the males began singing as if springtime had come to the sub-zero Canadian winter. The control group living in natural winter light was completely unchanged.

Light acts upon the bird through nerve impulses transmitted from the eyes to the brain and to the pituitary gland, which is located at the base of the brain and linked to it. The pituitary gland is especially sensitive to light. It is a master control, releasing into the bloodstream hormones that stimulate the secondary glands such as the thyroid and sex glands. They, in turn, release their own hormones that regulate the bird's inner body processes.

The thyroid gland controls the bird's energy supply, providing increased amounts during migration. Thus, when birds are held captive during their migration, their excess energy causes them to move in almost continual fidgets within their cage. They flap rapidly, making short flights in the direction they would fly if they were free. Back and forth, back and forth, fluttering incessantly, night migrants fidget by night and day migrants by day, burning the energy the thyroid releases.

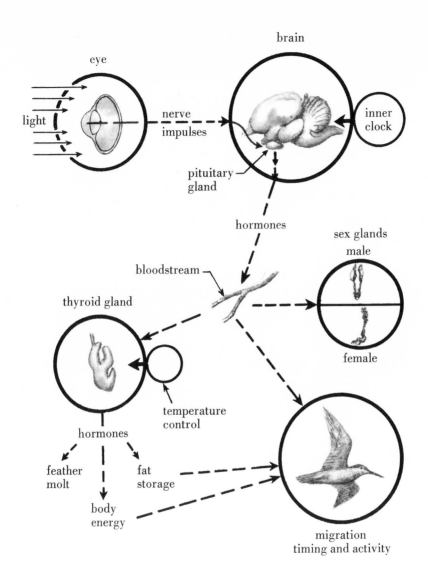

eye

brain

light

nerve
impulses

inner
clock

pituitary
gland

hormones

sex glands
male

bloodstream

female

thyroid gland

hormones

temperature
control

feather
molt

fat
storage

body
energy

migration
timing and activity

regulation of the bird's inner processes during migration

Fat storage before migration, as well as feather molt, are two other processes controlled by the thyroid on signals from the pituitary. The thyroid itself is very sensitive to temperature change, so that if the outside air temperature drops suddenly, it releases additional energy to make up for the extra loss of body heat. In this way, it keeps the bird's temperature constant. The effect is very much like that of a thermostat on a furnace, which regulates the amount of heat sent up according to the temperature in the house. This thermostat control by the thyroid probably determines the movements of weather migrants, north with warmth in spring, south with cold in autumn. Since it also probably controls reverse migrations, when severe cold occurs in the spring and unusual warmth in the autumn, the thyroid has the remarkable power to override the normal impulses of migration.

Although light can control the body processes, the connection between the outer and the inner clock is not always so direct and simple. In evolving their yearly schedules, each of the migrant species adapted to the outer clock in different ways. Some species seem to depend directly upon natural light for their timing; others seem to ignore it completely.

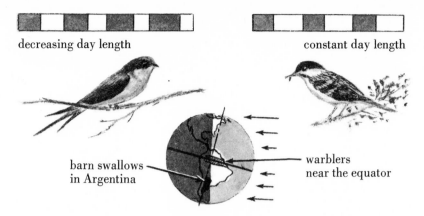

decreasing day length

constant day length

barn swallows
in Argentina

warblers
near the equator

spring departures that do not depend upon lengthening days

When warblers winter along the equator in northern Brazil, how do they receive a signal to prepare to fly north? Near the equator the change in day length throughout the year is less than one minute, surely not enough to schedule an inner cycle. Far below the equator, millions of barn swallows wintering in Argentina leave at the right time to intercept spring in their North American breeding grounds. But at the time they leave winter is approaching in the southern hemisphere, and the days are becoming shorter. The swallows certainly cannot be relying on increasing day length to prepare for their travels. All these species that winter near or below the equator must have a strong inner sense of time, independent of the days and nights in their winter quarters and in pace with the seasonal cycle in their breeding regions far to the north. Otherwise, they would not receive a signal telling them to fly.

The inner sense of time, or biological clock, of birds and other creatures is one of the great puzzles of nature that scientists around the world are now trying to solve. Although not very much is known about the operation of biological clocks, one thing is clear. Certain creatures, and especially migrant birds that travel long distances, often show an amazing independence of the natural cycle of day and night in their immediate location. When these birds are transported far from their normal habitat, or are put under constant artificial light, they persist in following their former schedules of eating, exercising, and sleeping. Their clocks have a strong, built-in rhythm and can run accurately for some time on their own.

Slender-billed shearwaters were transported during breeding season from the southern to the northern hemisphere. Despite the reversal of seasons, the shearwaters showed a strong tendency to keep to their normal breeding rhythm that they would have followed in the southern hemisphere. White storks carried from Europe across the equator to Peru bred at the same time as their fellow storks back home.

whitethroat

Probably the most amazing proof of the inner rhythm of birds came during studies of a group of European warblers called whitethroats. Taken from their nests before they were hatched, the whitethroats were raised in soundproof cages in complete isolation under artificial light. They could feed whenever they wanted. Although they had never seen the outside world and had no clues to the migratory schedule of their species, two of the birds showed flight fidgets at the exact time when wild whitethroats were migrating. Only the timing of their inner clocks, inherited from their parents, could have signaled the start of their migratory behavior.

The ability of these biological clocks to keep their own

time under changing conditions of light shows that some of the yearly activities of birds may not be connected directly to increasing or decreasing amounts of daylight. Most species of birds, including the juncos tested by Rowan, show an insensitivity to artificial shifts in day length for some months after breeding. Yet the autumn migrations take place exactly during this time. Probably the feather molt, storage of fat, and release of energy after breeding—all preparatory to the fall migration— are due to the automatic timing of the biological clock operating independently of outside factors.

The longest-traveling migrants, like the arctic tern, golden plover, slender-billed shearwater, and barn swallow, may be sensitive to the day-night cycle only during

nesting arctic tern

that part of the year when they are in their breeding grounds. Their clocks may be set at the time of nesting, then run on until the following year without resetting by the environment. If so, the times for molting, migrating, and mating may be signaled by their own inner rhythm. This theory would explain why birds wintering near the equator are able to migrate at the right times, even though the day length remains constant.

On the other hand, such migrants may have a way of totaling up the hours of daylight they are exposed to from the time they return to the South. Then they would depend more directly on the light in their particular winter quarters for the signal to fly north. Scientists differ on their answer to this problem, some inclined to believe that all bodily functions and migration movements are controlled by a preset biological clock, others feeling that the influence of day length acts to adjust the timing as the year goes on.

The general departure times of migrant birds are set by their inner clocks, but the actual departures are probably signaled by a combination of things. When enough body fat has been stored, when the weather and wind are favorable for travel, and, finally, when the psychological stimulation created by the sight of other birds flocking has exerted its effect, then the migration flights are triggered. As they travel birds continue to be affected by outside factors. Their accurate inner clocks urge them on toward their breeding grounds, but cold, strong wind, or rain can slow them down.

In all these ways, the inner time control of the biological clock is checked and balanced by the forces of the environment. The same pressures that through thousands of years acted to set the overall timing of migrations continue to affect the day-to-day movements of birds.

Inner timing of migrants
is checked and balanced by outside forces.

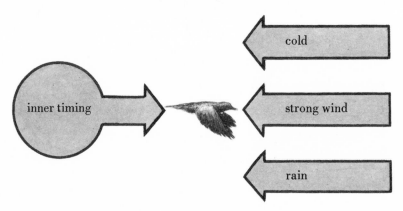

4   *Which Way Do They Fly?*

A migration route is not a fixed, precise pathway like a road or railroad. Nor is it like an air lane or sea-lane, a narrow invisible road across sky or sea, maintained by maps and highly accurate navigation. If it were, we could expect to see the same birds passing the same point during their travels, year after year. But the actual movements of most birds show that their semi-annual migration paths often shift considerably from one year to the next.

A migration route connects the breeding and wintering ranges of migrant birds. A route can be broad or narrow. Coming north from South America, cliff swallows follow the slim S-curve of the Isthmus of Panama into Mexico, while barn swallows often head directly across the broad waters of the Caribbean Sea. Since both birds feed aloft on insects, the only apparent reason for the different routes is that barn swallows, which travel

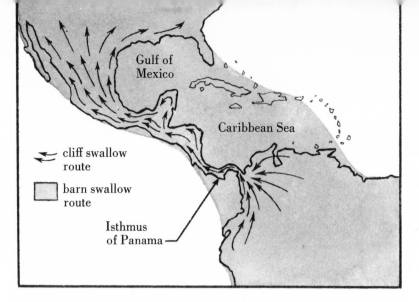

different routes of cliff swallows and barn swallows

longer distances, are stronger fliers and can cross the Caribbean and the Gulf of Mexico.

Food supply is an important factor in the determination of migration routes. Migrants must fly through regions where they can find proper food. Most shorebirds, like sandpipers and plovers, seek their food on coastal flats or the edges of rivers or lakes, so they usually avoid flying over unbroken expanses of forest. Most songbirds, on the other hand, search for their insect food in or below trees, so they normally do not travel across treeless plains or along sandy shores. However, within these restrictions of geography and terrain, the routes of most migrants are many miles wide, unlike the pathways of man.

Migration routes through the United States usually are described as four main flyways. They are the Atlantic, Mississippi, Central, and Pacific flyways, and they run through areas where many species are concentrated during migration. However, birds do not follow them as if they were some sort of aerial superhighway, for migration routes are much broader and more varied than the term flyway suggests. Birds travel in many directions and cross every square mile of the country. For example, redhead ducks, white-crowned sparrows, and other species make long east-west flights, contrary to the north-south directions of the flyways. White pelicans

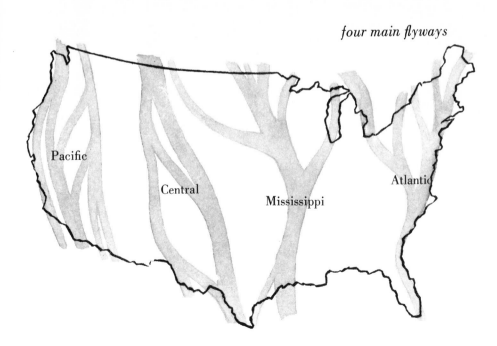

four main flyways

Pacific

Central

Mississippi

Atlantic

travel diagonally across country from northwest to south-east. All these species cross several flyways, so they are certainly migrating independently of them.

As the study of migrations has improved, scientists have become skeptical about the idea of flyways. Until recently, they thought that the Atlantic flyway was the main guiding line for all birds traveling through the easternmost United States. Birds were supposed to funnel along the coastline with little deviation. However, radar sightings from Cape Cod show that birds disregard the Atlantic shoreline and cross it readily to and from the sea. In autumn, songbirds have been seen on radar flying inland through New England toward the west on a very broad front rather than following the coast in a narrow line. Radar has also shown many birds offshore, moving southeast over the Atlantic on oceanic routes to South America. Earlier it had been assumed that only a few species in limited numbers flew this way. Now we know that large flights of warblers and other songbirds, as well as several kinds of sandpipers and plovers, head far out to sea.

Such findings show that we may oversimplify migration routes by thinking of them in terms of flyways. Although most birds crossing the continent probably move

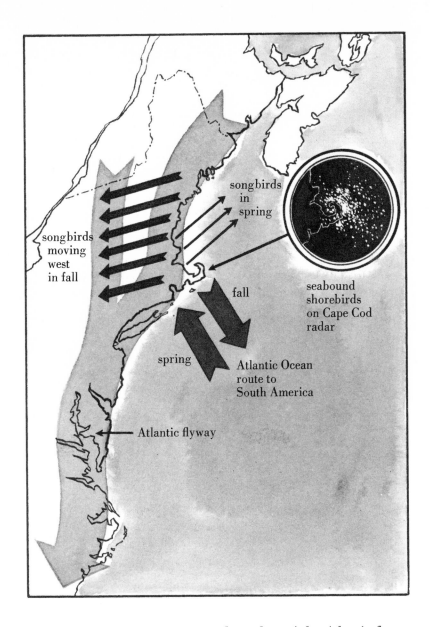

bird movements independent of the Atlantic flyway

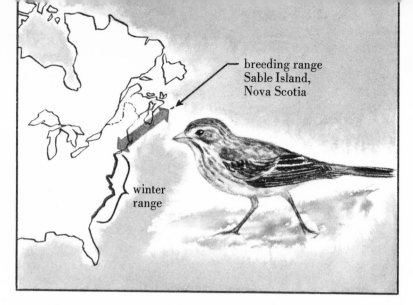

Ipswich sparrow

through these general areas of concentration, much more study of individual species is needed before a clear picture of the various routes can be drawn. For the present, a description of the overall patterns that migrating birds follow may be more helpful.

Most birds fly between their nesting and wintering ranges in a north-south direction, since this pattern is linked directly to seasonal change. Among the north-south migrants, the Ipswich sparrow travels the shortest distance. Colored like the beach dunes on which it lives, similar in size to the common song sparrow, the Ipswich is a much rarer bird. Of all true migrants, it has the smallest breeding range—the single point of Sable Island in Nova Scotia. To reach its winter home, the Ipswich moves south along the Atlantic coast as far as Georgia, a maximum distance of 1200 miles. However, individual birds are seen during the winter as far north as New York, so the winter range of the Ipswich, which stays within a quarter mile of the sea, is a long, thin line down the East Coast of the United States.

The rose-breasted grosbeak, which is slightly smaller than a robin, is one of the large group of medium-distance north-south migrants. From its nesting range in central Canada and the northeastern United States, it flies south about 2300 miles, crossing the Gulf of Mexico, to winter in the comfortable climate of Central America and northern South America.

rose-breasted grosbeak

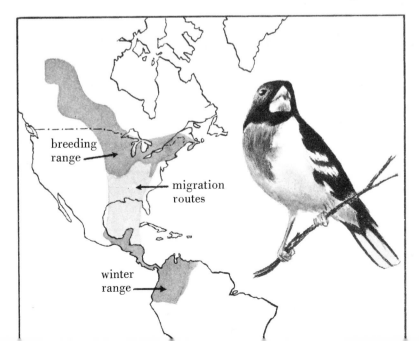

breeding range

migration routes

winter range

One of the longest traveling north-south migrants is the barn swallow. Graceful and strong in flight, it is often seen during migration skimming the waves far from land. The barn swallow's routes were known long before the use of more modern techniques of migration study. Thousands of sightings by different ground observers at widely scattered points were pieced together. By noting the dates of arrivals and departures in different regions during the year, scientists drew up a complete picture of the barn swallow's migration routes. It arrives in Louisiana around March 20, in Missouri about April 7, and in Saskatchewan, Canada, around April 30. Barn swallows nest in central Alaska, as well as all across Canada and the United States. In the winter they move south to central Argentina and Chile. A general rule is that individual birds, of a given species, which breed the farthest north also winter the farthest south. It is certainly true of the barn swallow, for some members of the species fly over 10,000 miles twice a year, traveling between Alaska and Argentina.

When one group of a species flies over other groups of its kin to reach breeding or wintering grounds, this movement is called leapfrog migration. All north-south migrants show this pattern, but in no other species can it be seen as clearly as among the Pacific coast fox sparrow.

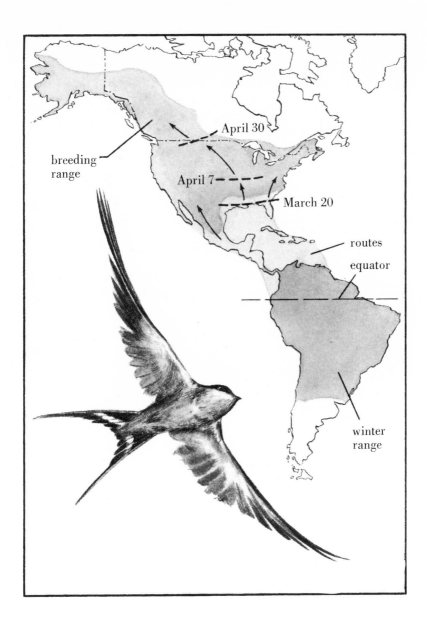

breeding
range

April 30

April 7

March 20

routes

equator

winter
range

barn swallow

There are six subspecies, or races, of this sparrow. One race does not migrate at all and both breeds and winters around Puget Sound, Washington. The second race breeds farther north and winters farther south, and the ranges of the other races diverge progressively. The race that migrates the longest distance breeds at the far end of the Aleutian Islands and winters south in California.

Although a north-south migration generally brings the greatest change in climate for the number of miles trav-

leapfrog migration of Pacific coast fox sparrows

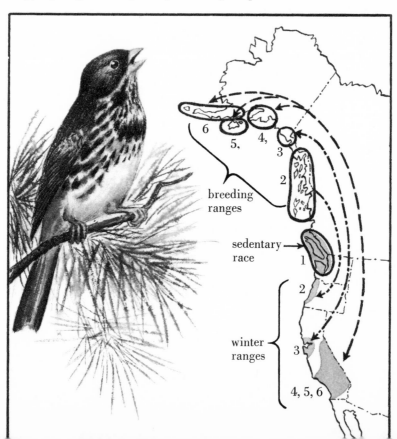

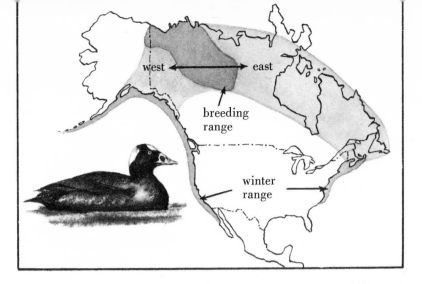

surf scoter

eled, some species move chiefly in east-west directions. One such bird is the surf scoter that nests in northwest Canada. It dives to eat mollusks on the lake bottoms, but in the subzero temperatures of the Canadian winter the lakes are locked deep in ice, so the scoters cannot feed. At this time of year some scoters fly east to winter along the northeastern coast of the United States, gathering mussels in the ice-free ocean. Other scoters fly west to the Pacific. A number of other species, such as canvasback and redhead ducks, evening grosbeaks, and snow buntings, also fly across country to escape the severe cold of the interior and winter closer to the warmer coastlines. All of these hardy birds can stand winter weather, but they need the slightly milder climate of the coast in order to find food.

East-west movements are not only made by species nesting inland and seeking warmer climate near the oceans during the winter. In fact, the longest east-west flights, spanning many thousands of miles, are sometimes combined with north-south routes. The bobolink is one bird that flies this pattern. From the grasslands of Bolivia, southern Brazil, and northern Argentina, far below the equator, bobolinks set out each spring on a long journey to nest in the northern United States and southern Canada. When they arrive in the United States they are east of the Mississippi River, but as spring advances they push farther and farther west across country until they almost reach the Pacific coast.

Originally the nesting range of the bobolinks was located in the eastern United States. As settlers in the United States moved westward, they made an expansion of this range possible. More and more land was turned into farms, and since the favorite habitat of bobolinks is a plowed or grassy field, they moved west along with the pioneers. Today their migration retraces the path of this range expansion years ago.

One might think that those bobolinks nesting in the far West would fly directly to South America in autumn, traveling the shortest route through Mexico. Instead, the

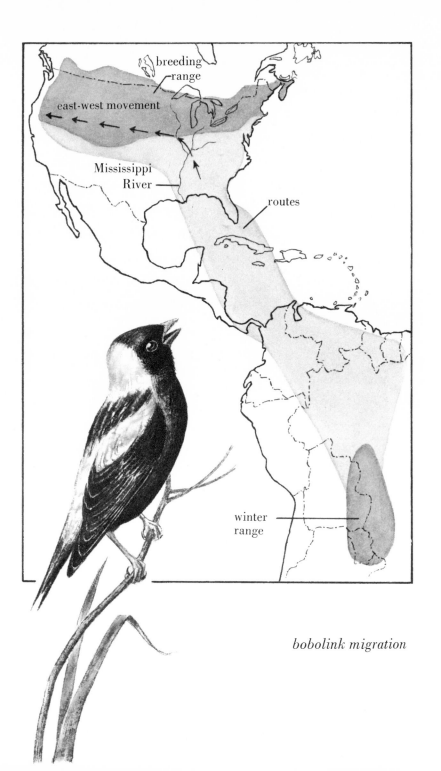

breeding range

east-west movement

Mississippi River

routes

winter range

bobolink migration

entire population flies east, at least as far as the Mississippi Valley, where they join the rest of their kin and
move south with them along the ancestral pathway. Such
an indirect return to the southern wintering grounds is
fairly common. The pattern appears whenever a great east-
west expansion of the nesting range has occurred. Most
of these continental population expansions happened
thousands of years ago. In the case of the bobolink, however, man fortunately has been able to witness and record
the movement.

Another sweeping east-west movement within the
northern breeding range is made by the wheatear, a bird
the size of the sparrow. Wheatears winter in Africa, flying
north in spring as far as Europe. There they divide in a
great forking movement. One group heads west across the
Atlantic Ocean, flying non-stop 1200 miles from the British Isles to Iceland. From there they continue to the arctic
regions of Canada. The other group flies east across the
Balkan countries and nests along the top of the Asian continent and Alaska. The two groups travel around the globe
and almost meet in northern Canada.

After breeding, the wheatears return to winter quarters
in a way similar to the long flight of the bobolink. The
birds in Canada retrace their perilous path across the At-

lantic, while those nesting in Alaska and Asia backtrack across Europe to reach Africa. Wheatears from southern Africa nesting in Alaska travel at least 22,000 miles round trip each year. Their maximum north-south distance from southern Africa to the island of Spitzbergen is about 6500 miles, while their east-west distance is about 9000 miles. This pattern that the wheatears fly shows that north-south and east-west routes are not rigid lines of travel, but may be combined in a number of variations.

wheatear

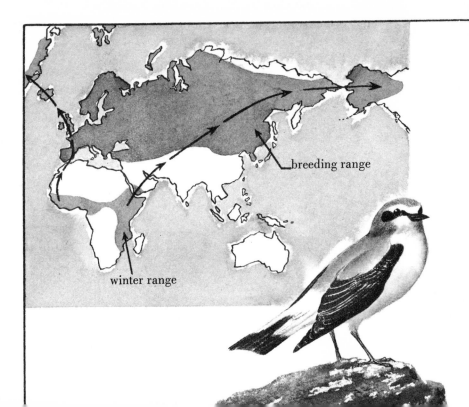

breeding range

winter range

Most migrants follow the same path to and from their nesting grounds. One exception is the Atlantic population of the American golden plover, a shorebird that nests in the Canadian arctic and winters in southeastern South America. Late every summer, fattened on insects, these birds set out southward from the coasts of Labrador, Nova Scotia, and the northeastern United States, flying on and on down the Atlantic Ocean. Two days and two nights later, after a non-stop journey of over 2400 miles, they reach the northern coast of South America on the way to their wintering grounds on the pampas of Argentina. In spring, the plovers do not return by the same route. Instead, they fly across the Caribbean Sea and up through central United States. Such a pattern, in which the northern route is widely separated from the southern route, is called a loop migration.

One reason for the plovers' loop migration is the need to avoid the late, cold spring climate in northeastern Canada caused by the chilling Labrador ocean current. Along the warmer inland route, the golden plovers find more insect food to replenish their energy reserves on their journey to the north. Another possible cause of their loop is the direction of the prevailing winds they meet on their flight. Above forty degrees north latitude, west winds

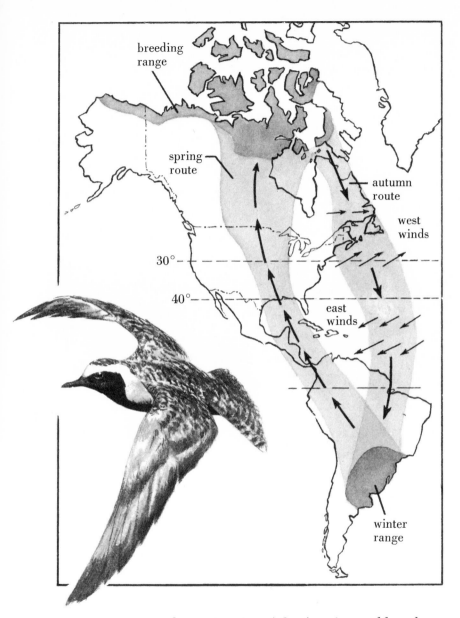

breeding
range

spring
route

autumn
route

west
winds

30°

40°

east
winds

winter
range

loop migration of the American golden plover

blow, while east winds prevail south of thirty degrees. By flying southeast over the ocean, plovers appear to take fullest advantage of the prevailing westerlies. By changing course south of thirty degrees, they can benefit from the easterly trade winds. To fly with tail winds on their trip north, however, the plovers would have to reverse these directions, thus creating the loop. Further study may prove that all loop migrations are determined by the available food supply and the prevailing winds.

Still another kind of movement is called a split migration. It occurs when different groups of the same species migrate along different routes. Among the birds that fly this pattern are the famous white storks of Europe, cherished and protected by the townspeople as traditional bringers of babies and good luck. They nest, often on high chimneys and steeples, in Spain, Holland, the Rhine River regions of Germany and France, and in central and eastern Europe. On rising thermals, these long-legged, long-necked gliders soar southward each autumn, but in different directions. Storks from Holland and France move southwest together with their relatives from Spain, flying toward Gibraltar. Those in the area roughly east of the Rhine River fly southeastward toward the narrow waters of the Bosporus, at Istanbul, Turkey.

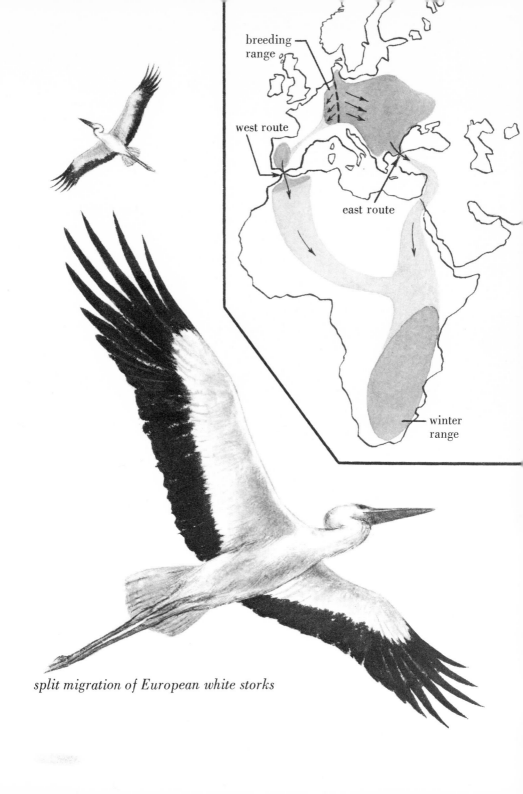

breeding range

west route

east route

winter range

split migration of European white storks

Because they rely on thermals, which are generated by the sun heating the earth, storks rarely start across open water unless they can see the other side, and so they avoid flying the full distance across the Mediterranean. Instead, they circle around it on the eastern and western ends. When the western storks reach Gibraltar, they gain great height by circling upward in thermals, then glide across to the opposite shore, continuing on to their winter quarters by way of western Africa. The eastern group, after crossing the Bosporus, moves down through Asia Minor into Africa. Some of the white storks travel as far as the Cape of Good Hope, 8000 miles from their nest.

Most migrants change their climate by changing their latitude. Some, however, change their altitude instead. In the springtime, they fly up from the warmer valleys where they winter to their nesting grounds near the colder peaks of mountains. This movement is called vertical, or alti-

vertical migrations of water pipits

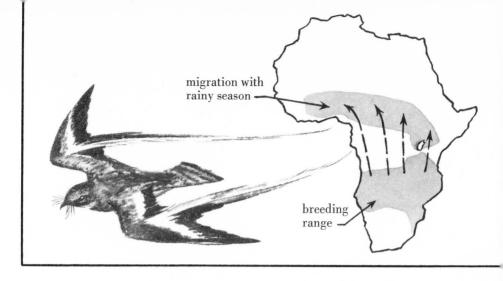

pennant-winged nightjar

tudinal, migration. In some parts of the United States, the water pipit migrates this way. A bird that is the size of a sparrow, it flies up thousands of feet to nest in the Rocky Mountains of Colorado. However, there is only a limited amount of space on the upper mountain slopes for nesting and feeding, and most pipits must travel about 2000 miles north to the Canadian tundra to find suitable nesting grounds.

Even birds that remain in the tropics all year round may migrate from one area to another. This movement seems to be connected with the abundance or scarcity of certain foods caused by the dry and rainy seasons. In Africa, the pennant-winged nightjar follows the rainy season through different regions, feeding on winged termites and other insects that swarm with the onset of the rains.

Wings, Sun, and Stars

Of the many migrations that take place over the oceans, one of the most unusual is made by the arctic tern. Although it is not an oceanic species, this bird travels over vast stretches of sea and is perhaps the most spectacular long-distance migrant of all. By the early part of this century, arctic terns were known to be nesting at the top of the globe, for one nest had been found only 450 miles from the North Pole. It was also known that they traveled each year to winter near Antarctica, but which way they flew remained unknown until the recovery of several birds that had been banded revealed the routes.

In July, 1913, many young arctic terns were lifted from their nests on the crowded colony at Eastern Egg Rock, Maine, and banded. In August, 1917, one of the banded terns was found dead on a beach in the Niger River Delta, West Africa. Thus, one point between the arctic and antarctic had been established. Ten years later a bird banded at Turnevik Bay, Labrador, in July, 1927, turned up the following October at La Rochelle, France. Another Labrador bird, banded in July, 1928, was picked up the following November near Natal, South Africa, after traveling about 9000 miles across the Atlantic to Europe and down along the entire west coast of Africa. Evidently the arctic tern crossed the Atlantic regularly

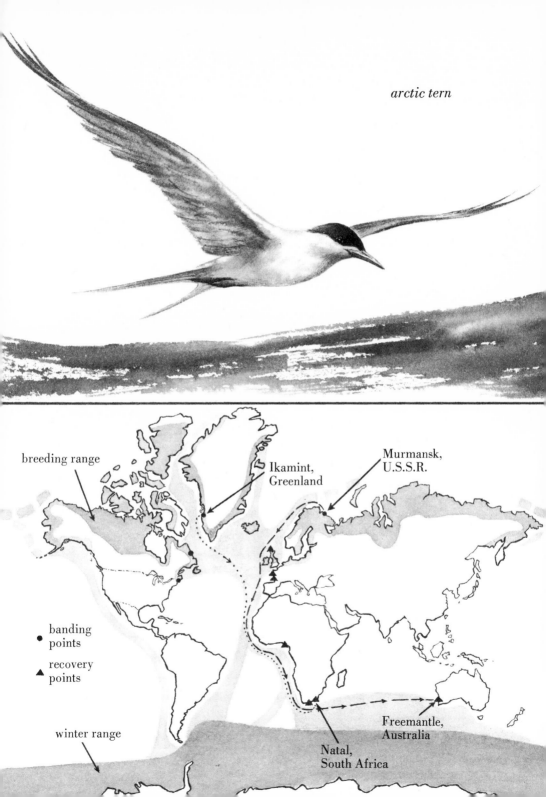

arctic tern

breeding range

Ikamint,
Greenland

Murmansk,
U.S.S.R.

banding
points

recovery
points

winter range

Natal,
South Africa

Freemantle,
Australia

between the United States and the coasts of Europe and Africa.

Other recoveries added to the picture, and sightings revealed another route down the Pacific coast of North and South America. In 1951, the longest bird flight then known was recorded when an arctic tern banded in July at Ikamint, Greenland, was found in October at Natal, South Africa. Its slim-pointed wings had carried it more than 11,000 miles in less than three months. Most amazing of all was the flight of a tern banded in July, 1955, near Murmansk, in the northern Soviet Union. It was discovered in May, 1956, on a beach near Freemantle, Australia. Since arctic terns do not migrate inland, this bird must have circled western Europe, flown down along the west coast of Africa to the Cape of Good Hope, then continued across the Indian Ocean, a total distance of at least 14,000 miles. Taken all together, these recoveries clearly demonstrated the incredible yearly round trip of about 25,000 miles made between the top and the bottom of the globe by the arctic tern and traced its far-flung routes over the world's oceans.

The truly oceanic birds, which spend almost their entire life on the open sea, are the petrels, shearwaters, and albatrosses. They touch land only once a year to nest on

black-footed albatrosses

remote coasts and islands. After a brief period spent rais-
ing their young, they head out to sea again and do not
return to land until the next breeding season. Not sur-
prisingly, the migrations of oceanic birds are the most
difficult to study. Unlike land birds and shorebirds, they
do not have a fixed winter range. They constantly move
during most of the year across unmarked seas, where few
observers are present.

One ornithologist, however, took many sightings of Wilson's petrels from all parts of the Atlantic Ocean and pieced together their migration pattern. These birds nest on ocean islands between South America and Antarctica. During March and April, autumn below the equator, they move north into the tropical part of the South Atlantic. By June they have swung farther north along the offshore waters of the eastern United States, sleeping on the swells, riding out storms, pattering over the surface with webbed feet while feeding. During midsummer, they spread across the entire width of the North Atlantic from New England to West Africa. By October they pass the western coasts of Africa and begin to return diagonally across the South Atlantic toward their nesting grounds. On this circuit around the Atlantic, these dainty sea walkers travel over 20,000 miles each year.

This particular loop migration around the Atlantic is caused by a combination of prevailing wind directions and the location of food-rich ocean currents. Oceanic birds tend to avoid warm surface waters and fly instead with the cold currents in which small fish and crustaceans are more abundant. Their routes often coincide with the food "veins" that the great whale herds of the past followed during their own migrations.

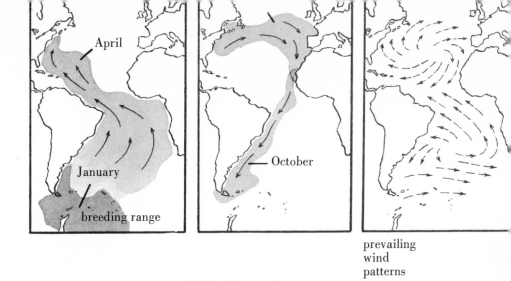

April

January

breeding range

October

prevailing
wind
patterns

oceanic loop migration of Wilson's petrels

Another oceanic species, the slender-billed shearwater, clearly uses the prevailing winds during its great yearly sweep around the entire North Pacific Ocean. Each Southern autumn, spring above the equator, they leave their breeding grounds on the coast and offshore islands of southeast Australia and New Zealand. Striking out northward over the Pacific along the island chain of Japan and up past Alaska through the Bering Straits, they arrive in June in the East Siberian Sea. By August they are moving southeast across the Aleutian Islands and down along the California coast. Then they turn southwestward and fly across the width of the Pacific, winging in true shearwater style, skimming through the troughs of waves, alighting once in a while to rest and feed. One shipboard observer witnessed their migration flight. First, a dark billowing cloud appeared on the horizon. Then it became apparent that a great flock of birds was approaching. For an hour and a half they passed in a dense stream hundreds of feet high and a thousand feet wide, an estimated 150 million shearwaters.

Flying with the prevailing winds almost the entire way, the slender-billed shearwaters make an immense loop of about 21,000 miles around the Pacific to reach their breeding grounds again in September. Just how dependent they

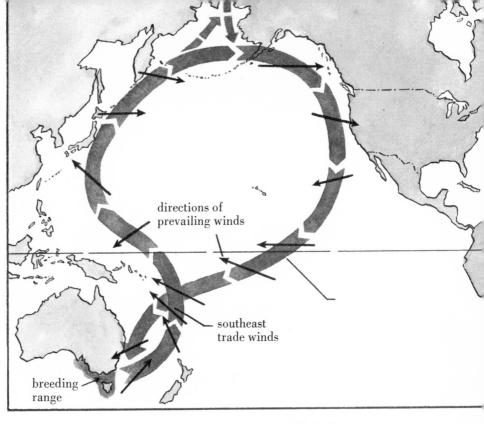

directions of
prevailing winds

southeast
trade winds

breeding
range

loop migration of slender-billed shearwaters

are upon favorable winds may be seen in the one region
where the shearwaters must fly against the wind. This area
is off the northeast corner of Australia, where strong
southeast trade winds blow year round. At times many
homebound shearwaters, especially the young birds, are
lost as they try to fight their way against the severe head
winds. Their urge to return punctually to their ancestral
breeding grounds seems to become very intense as they
near their destination. Instead of resting on the ocean

when tired, they may throw all their energy into battling the wind, and many of them die from exhaustion and drowning.

The greatest ocean traveler of all is probably the wandering albatross. With a wing span of up to fourteen feet, it is an oceanic soarer, deriving flight power from the differences in wind speed at different heights above the surface. By first gliding on a downwind slope to pick up speed, then turning into the wind to regain height, repeating the same maneuvers again and again, the wanderer can travel for days without flapping once. Its size and method of flight limit its range to the "roaring forties," a world-wide belt of strong prevailing west winds between forty and fifty degrees south latitude. After nesting on such southern ocean islands as Tristan da Cunha, Kerguelen, and South Georgia, the wandering albatrosses depart, setting their wings into the sea wind. How far do they travel? Banding returns on birds that nest on tiny islands and travel over immense stretches of ocean are scarce, but there are a few.

In 1887 a boy in Freemantle, Australia, found a dead wandering albatross on the beach with a tin band around its neck. Punched into the metal was an appeal for help from a shipwrecked crew on the Crozet Islands, 3500

wandering albatross

Freemantle, Australia

"roaring forties"

west winds

40°

50°

Crozet Islands

Kerguelen Island

Cape Horn

miles to the west, dated only two weeks before. When a rescue party was sent out, it found that the crew had run out of food and left the Crozets in desperation, never to be heard from again. A wandering albatross banded on Kerguelen Island was recovered over 9500 miles to the east by a French ship near Cape Horn. The time between banding and recovery was about three years, so the complete mileage totaled by this bird was almost impossible to estimate. A wanderer banded as a chick on Kerguelen in July, 1952, was found dead on the coast at Patache, Chile, in October, 1953. Allowing for the prevailing winds on its route, this bird must have flown about 11,200 miles.

Impressive as such recoveries are, they only hint at the travels of wandering albatrosses. Indications are that they migrate around the world within the "roaring forties." How many miles they actually cover in one year, how many times they circle the earth in their lifetime, is not known. When more accurate information becomes available, the arctic tern may have to take second place as the greatest long-distance migrant.

From the limited movements of Ipswich sparrows to the world-wide ocean journeys of wandering albatrosses, the variety and extent of migration routes are astounding. But the routes are not eternally fixed and unchanging. All birds live under constant pressure, both favorable and unfavorable, from their natural and man-made environment, so marked changes in their routes and ranges continually occur.

Storms, for example, have affected migrations. A flock of European fieldfares, relatives of American robins, were caught by a storm during their migration from Norway to England. Gale winds carried them all the way west across the Atlantic Ocean to northeastern Greenland. Two weeks later all the fieldfares had moved down to the warmer southern tip of Greenland, where they remained

Storms affect bird migration.

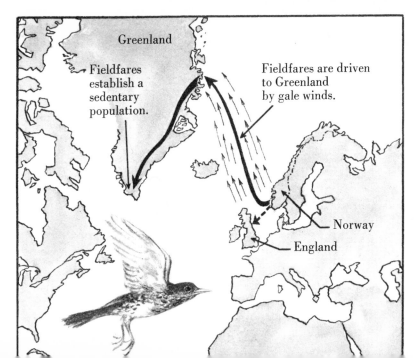

Greenland

Fieldfares establish a sedentary population.

Fieldfares are driven to Greenland by gale winds.

Norway

England

and established a sedentary population. Although the climate of Greenland was harsh, the hazards of trying to escape were probably worse.

Migrant birds retreat and relocate in the face of constant adverse forces, just as they expand and thrive when conditions allow. The routes and ranges of migration are part of a living, continually changing process, subject to the laws of nature, but dependent also upon the actions of man.

5 *How Do They Find Their Way?*

Every spring and fall billions of birds cross hundreds and thousands of miles between their nesting and wintering grounds. Over jungles, mountains, plains, oceans, and cities they fly, slowed by wind and rain, pushed aside by storms, and threatened by sudden cold. With no navigation instruments, except what nature has packed into their feathered skulls, migrating birds manage to find their way. Do they travel by chance, pointing their beaks in some general direction and flying until they reach a likely nesting place? Or do they navigate with great accuracy along definite paths toward specific destinations?

One way to find out is by conducting homing experiments. Homing is the ability of a bird to find its way back to the nest from which it has been taken, and this ability is not limited to wild migrant birds. Indeed, the most famous homers of all—racing pigeons—are domestic sedentary birds.

In a homing experiment, migrant birds are taken from their nests and transported in lightproof boxes so that they cannot see and possibly remember their surroundings en route. Released at distances of hundreds and sometimes thousands of miles from their nests, in regions they could never have seen before, some birds manage to find their way home. In such tests, the time that a bird takes to return is directly related to the accuracy of its navigation. Allowing for other factors, such as weather conditions, the speed of the return flight indicates how well the bird can tell where it is upon being released and which is the way to fly to reach home.

Usually, if the distance between the nest and the point of release is increased in a series of experiments, fewer and fewer birds manage to return. To explain this result, scientists have suggested that birds do not head in any special direction upon release, but simply scatter haphazardly, then hold a fairly steady course until they either reach or fail to reach familiar territory. As the birds are released farther away, the angle between the release point and the home territory becomes smaller. Thus, fewer birds will chance to fly along a correct course, and the number of birds reaching home will decrease. If true, this theory would mean that birds travel with no sense of where they are going.

theory of random scatter

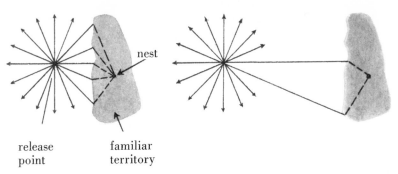

release
point

familiar
territory

nest

As distance of release is increased, fewer birds return.

Another similar theory is based on a mathematical formula that describes the random movement of gas molecules. If one assumes that birds behave like gas molecules, then they will fly, after release, in one direction for a certain distance, turning at random to follow another direction. Eventually, by heading this way and that way, flying at an easy pace for a certain time each day, birds may be able to reach their home. When the results of homing experiments were checked by this formula, they showed that most birds were using no more sense of direction than molecules of gas moving at random.

However, neither the possibility of random scatter or random search could account for the better homing results

theory of random search

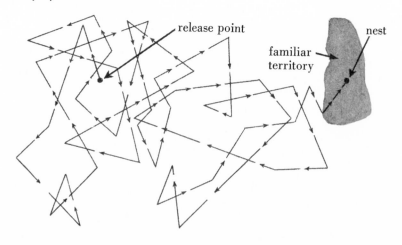

produced by certain species. Herring gulls, for example, returned home in large numbers from as far away as 500 miles. Even at 900 miles, two thirds of the birds released found their nest. Yet, even in these tests, the gulls could have returned home within the times recorded on their tests by using scatter or search.

Do birds need any further navigational ability to travel? Arctic terns reach Antarctica and golden plovers arrive in Hawaii, crossing thousands of miles of ocean on the way. These flights suggest that at least some species find their way by design. Yet without the knowledge of their behavior during the whole flight, no one could be sure. Although experimenters watched birds with binoculars after they were released in homing tests, they merely saw what they did in the first few minutes. The only way to be sure of what the birds did during the rest of the flight was to fly with them.

Accordingly, Donald Griffin, an American scientist, learned how to pilot a light plane in order to follow homing birds. A helper released a bird from the ground while

Griffin circled overhead; then he flew along behind it. Herring gulls were the first species Griffin experimented with, and in 1940 he was able to follow some of them for ten to fifteen miles. The gulls did not start flying directly toward their nests, but seemed to head in any number of directions. Clearly they did not know where their nests were in relation to their strange location. Griffin could not be sure if the birds were scattering, using random search, or working along some more definite pattern, since sea gulls are soaring birds and often depart from a direct path to search out thermal currents.

Griffin next tried gannets, large white seabirds with a wing span of six feet, which nest along the high rocky cliffs of eastern Canada. The color and large size of these birds made them easy to follow against blue sea or green forest below. Griffin took gannets from their nesting grounds on Bonaventure Island and carried them to Caribou, Maine, which was one hundred miles from the sea in any direction. By removing the birds from their normal range along the shore, he could be pretty sure that they would not use remembered landmarks to find their way. In the tests, the gannets flew more directly than the gulls, detouring less to hunt for thermals. But still keeping them in sight was very difficult, since they had an uncooperative

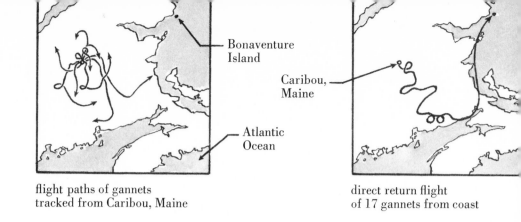

flight paths of gannets
tracked from Caribou, Maine

Bonaventure
Island

Caribou,
Maine

Atlantic
Ocean

direct return flight
of 17 gannets from coast

airplane tracking of homing gannets

habit of soaring so high that they vanished into the bases of the clouds.

Nevertheless, Griffin managed to follow nine gannets one at a time part of the way back to Bonaventure over distances between 25 to 230 miles. The longest flight took nine strenuous hours of constant maneuvering above and around the bird, while an assistant checked landmarks and mapped the course. Just when they came within sight of the Atlantic coast, and the gannet started a downward glide, Griffin had to turn back. The plane's extra fuel tanks had not been filled, and so they could not tell if the bird was able to get its bearings toward home upon reaching the more familiar coast.

None of the gannets had showed a definite pattern of search, and their flights, although not so aimless as to be called wandering, showed almost no sense of homeward direction. However, two years later, after releasing a group of seventeen gannets at Caribou, Griffin succeeded in following them all the way to Bonaventure. The birds explored in a way similar to that of the single gannets, but once they reached the seacoast they headed quickly and directly toward home. Griffin concluded that searching for familiar terrain was the method used by gannets in strange territory.

The visual memory demonstrated by the gannets had been observed in the behavior of other birds. In one earlier test, pigeons were trained to peck at a certain spot on an aerial photograph of a landscape by giving them a food reward when they touched the proper point. Four years after they had last seen the photograph, it was presented to them again. Still they remembered to peck at the original spot.

While testing sea gulls, Griffin himself had made an interesting discovery. He released the same three gulls from the same point, about 240 miles from their nests, two years in a row. In the second year, the gulls took only one sixth as long to find their way back home. Apparently they had remembered landmarks from the first flight and were depending upon visual memory to return home the second time. Not only memory, but the ability to learn was involved. The longer time of the first flight was spent in some kind of searching. But on the second flight the birds must have eliminated many wrong turns and used those landmarks that earlier proved to be most helpful.

Wings, Sun, and Stars

The possibility that birds may have a sensitive, long-lasting visual memory suggests that they follow their migration routes by remembering important landmarks such as rivers, large lakes, mountains, or cities. This kind of mental filmstrip, which might be replayed during later trips, would be different from the simpler memory of a nesting region over which the bird flies any number of times. Instead of a pattern of the lay of the land, the memory of a route would require the use of landmarks as successive checkpoints and would include changes of direction along the way. Birds of different species would use such a visual memory in different ways. Day-traveling

land birds, able to watch the ground constantly, probably could rely on it much more than night migrants or oceanic migrants, which travel for long periods of time with no possibility of checking landmarks.

The ability of a bird or any other creature to choose a certain direction of travel, setting its course by means of cues from its surrounding environment, is called orientation. When the cues come from memory of the terrain, the method is known as landmark orientation. It was used by the homing gannets in directing themselves swiftly toward home from the familiar Atlantic coast. It is the simplest way to travel, so that given a choice birds will probably use it in preference to any other.

Certain migrant species that travel very long distances, including barn swallows, chimney swifts, and ospreys, return year after year to the same small nesting areas, and even to the same nests. Regardless of how they may guide themselves over the long stretches, the courses they follow are unlikely to be accurate enough to pinpoint their nest sites from thousands of miles away. Once they reach a general breeding area with which they are familiar, they almost certainly rely on landmarks to locate an island, a lake, a valley, a building, or a tree, on which they find their nest.

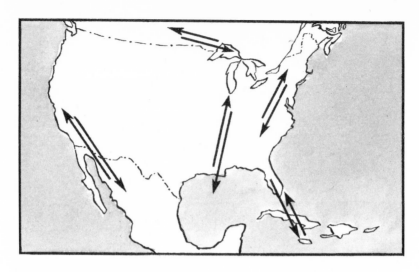

Migrant birds follow reversed
compass directions in spring and fall.

Nevertheless, the theory that birds find their way by landmark orientation fails to explain how migrants can continue to fly in a consistent flight direction day after day. In spring they are able to hold a north, northwest, or northeast course, and in autumn they reverse their heading. There must be some sense of direction, or compass orientation, that enables migrant birds to wake up in the morning and immediately start along the same course that they have been following. Often birds demonstrate this ability despite landscape features, such as rivers and coastlines, that would tend to steer them in other directions.

124

How Do They Find Their Way?

William Rowan, the biologist who had reset the inner clock of the juncos so that they were ready to breed in midwinter, conducted experiments on compass direction. Rowan captured some young crows in Alberta and held them until all the other crows had moved south to their winter quarters in the United States. Later he released the young ones, and many of them were recovered along the same southward migration route followed by their elders a month or so earlier. Although they never before had seen the areas over which they flew, the young crows chose the correct compass direction completely on their own.

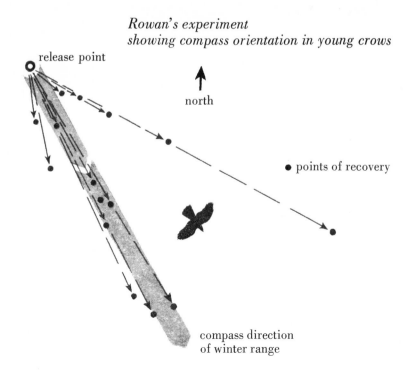

*Rowan's experiment
showing compass orientation in young crows*

release point

north

● points of recovery

compass direction
of winter range

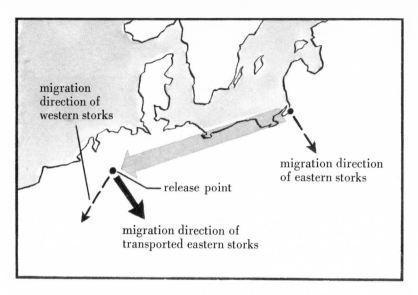

compass orientation of young white storks

The European white storks also demonstrated an ability to use compass orientation during their migration. Young storks from eastern Europe, which would normally migrate to the southeast around the eastern end of the Mediterranean, were transported to western Germany and held until all the local storks had left in a southwest direction for Africa. Upon their release, instead of following the southwest heading of the local birds, the eastern storks flew in the same southeast direction that they would have taken in their native region. Like the young crows, they showed a compass orientation independent of any older birds, but they also completely disregarded a shift in their geographic location hundreds of miles to the west. Both the crows and the storks had followed a compass direction that they had not learned, but one that they had inherited from their parents. Many other species have also been observed using compass direction.

In the late 1940's, a young scientist named Gustav Kramer in Wilhelmshaven, Germany, found a way of testing the orientation of migratory birds held in captivity. He used several starlings, captured while very young and carefully raised, which had become accustomed to living in cages. Kramer designed a circular cage, with no fixed details outside it that the birds could use as visual cues. A circular perch in the center of the cage allowed the bird being tested to head in any direction it chose. The floor of

Kramer orientation cage

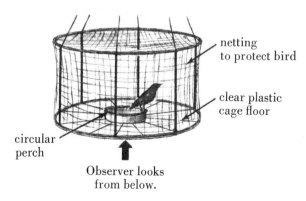

netting
to protect bird

clear plastic
cage floor

circular
perch

Observer looks
from below.

the cage was made of clear plastic and divided by lines into equal sectors. Stationed beneath the floor, where the bird could not see him, Kramer checked its position every ten seconds, by noting down the sector in which the bird happened to be at that moment.

Testing one especially tame starling, Kramer noticed that during the normal period of starling migration, early October, the bird continually took short fluttering hops inside the cage and pointed in a southwest direction. These flight fidgets lasted as long as the migration period, and the bird's heading corresponded to the migration direction of free starlings. Kramer tried to disturb the bird's heading by changing its surroundings. He rotated the cage. He took it to different areas around Wilhelmshaven. He surrounded it with a fence, so the starling could see only the sky above. The bird continued to hold its southwest heading. Thinking that the bird might be using the earth's magnetic field to direct itself, he put piles of iron nearby and ran strong electrical currents next to the cage. Still the starling kept heading southwest. At last Kramer concluded that its only directional cues must have been coming from the sky above.

To check this theory, Kramer put the cage inside a six-sided pavilion with windows that could be closed by shutters. Mirrors could be attached to the windows to change the angle of the light coming in. Kramer first left all the windows open so that light could enter on all sides. Since the time was spring, and the starling immediately headed northeast and held that direction during its fidgets, he knew that the house was not upsetting the bird's compass orientation, even though it could see only small areas of sky through the windows.

Next Kramer, using the mirrors, shifted the angle of light entering the window by ninety degrees. Thus, the starling did not see the sky directly outside, but instead saw areas of sky at right angles to the windows. When Kramer shifted the light ninety degrees in a clockwise direction, the bird changed its heading by ninety degrees in the same way. A ninety-degree counterclockwise light shift caused the starling to change its direction accordingly. The bird was clearly using the sun as its cue for orientation.

Although this experiment showed that the starling reacted to the sun's position, the question remained whether it could adjust its heading to the sun's changing position during the day. During their normal migration flights, starlings travel for at least six hours daily. If a northbound starling were to start flying at 8 A.M., the sun would be ninety degrees to its right. If it continued to fly at the same angle to the sun, it would be flying due east by noon. As the afternoon went on it would be heading further and further south, opposite to its original course.

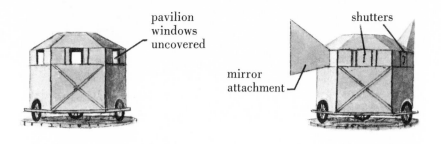

pavilion
windows
uncovered

shutters

mirror
attachment

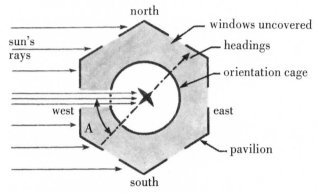

north

sun's
rays

west

east

A

south

windows uncovered

headings

orientation cage

pavilion

normal headings with normal light direction

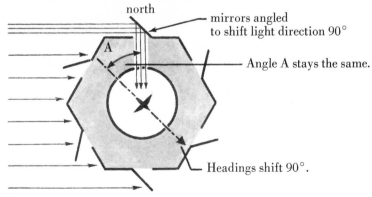

north

A

mirrors angled
to shift light direction 90°

Angle A stays the same.

Headings shift 90°.

Headings change with shift in light direction.

Kramer's experiment showing sun-compass orientation

To test whether the starling could allow for the changing position of the sun, Kramer devised another ingenious experiment. This time he used a cage surrounded by a screen, so the birds inside could see only the sky. Around the cage were twelve identical feeders, covered in front by slotted rubber sheets, so the birds could not see which one contained food. Then he proceeded to train the starlings to find food in a certain compass direction at a certain time of day. For example, only when a bird tried the east feeder at 8 A.M. would it find food. After two or three weeks it learned to seek food at 8 A.M. by always heading east toward the sun.

Then Kramer tested the trained birds at other times when the sun was in a different position. When a starling was signaled to look for food at 6 P.M., the bird allowed for the sun's western position and headed east, opposite from the sun. Again and again Kramer found that the starlings could allow for the sun's movement during the day, so that they could head in the right compass direction. In nature, this sun compass, as Kramer called it, would enable birds to hold a steady course for hours during migration.

Next Kramer wanted to check the effect of a bird's inner clock upon its sun compass. He took a starling

Kramer's feeding experiment

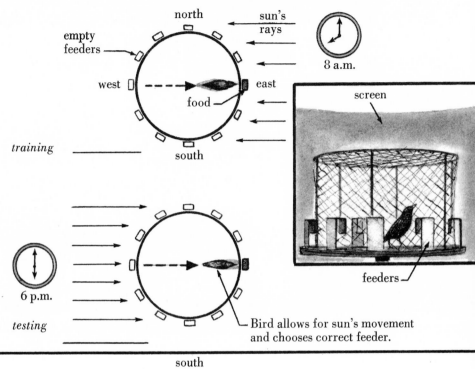

north

sun's rays

8 a.m.

empty feeders

west

east

food

training

south

screen

6 p.m.

testing

Bird allows for sun's movement and chooses correct feeder.

feeders

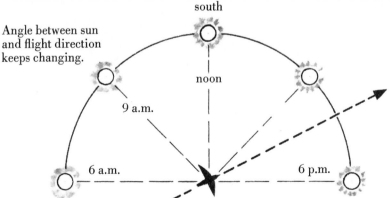

south

Angle between sun and flight direction keeps changing.

noon

9 a.m.

6 a.m.

6 p.m.

Birds follow a course by allowing for sun motion.

trained to seek food to the east at noon when the sun was ninety degrees to its right. By exposing it to artificially shifted periods of light and dark, he reset its clock six hours behind the local time. Upon testing it, he found that its headings were way off. The six-hour shift caused the starling to perceive noon when it was actually 6 P.M., and it headed south when it should have gone east. In this southerly position, the sun was still ninety degrees to its right, the correct training angle. The error had come from setting the inner clock back six hours, shifting the bird's orientation ninety degrees clockwise.

When the starling's inner clock was set six hours ahead, the bird's orientation shifted ninety degrees counterclockwise. When it perceived noon, it was actually 6 A.M., and it headed north when it should have gone east. In this northerly position the sun again was at the training angle, ninety degrees to the right, and the heading error came from shifting the clock. Thus, Kramer showed that the bird's inner clock was essential to its sun-compass orientation.

Sun-compass orientation probably accounts for the ability of most day migrants to find their way, especially when used together with the memory of landmarks. But what of those countless birds traveling by night? Could they

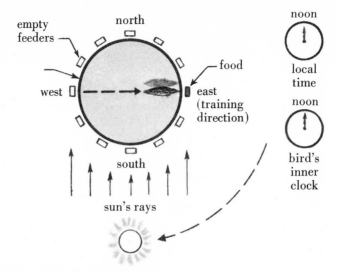

empty feeders

north

food

west

east (training direction)

south

sun's rays

noon

local time

noon

bird's inner clock

training—with normal inner clock

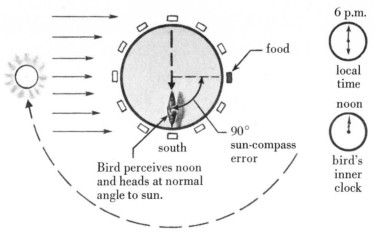

food

90° sun-compass error

south

Bird perceives noon and heads at normal angle to sun.

6 p.m.

local time

noon

bird's inner clock

testing—with inner clock shifted back six hours

Kramer's experiment showing the dependence of the sun-compass upon the inner clock possibly be using the stars as their guide? Using cages like those designed by Kramer, another young German, Franz Sauer, set out to study the orientation of night migrants.

The night migrants Sauer selected for his tests were European warblers, which are much more difficult to keep in captivity than starlings. He and his wife painstakingly raised their own birds, babying them more than any mother bird would have. In their cage the birds had a completely natural view of the night sky. During both the spring and fall migration periods, Sauer's warblers took the same headings under the night sky as their relatives that were free to travel. In two cases, warblers that had been raised from eggs in complete isolation began their flight fidgets at the right time and took correct headings under a sky they were seeing for the first time. Like the young crows and white storks, their timing and orientation must have been inherited.

Next Sauer took the warblers indoors, under the artificial sky of the planetarium dome at the Bremen Naval School. During the spring and fall migration periods, their headings were the same under the dome as they had been under the natural sky. Thus, Sauer concluded that the warblers were using star-compass orientation. When he

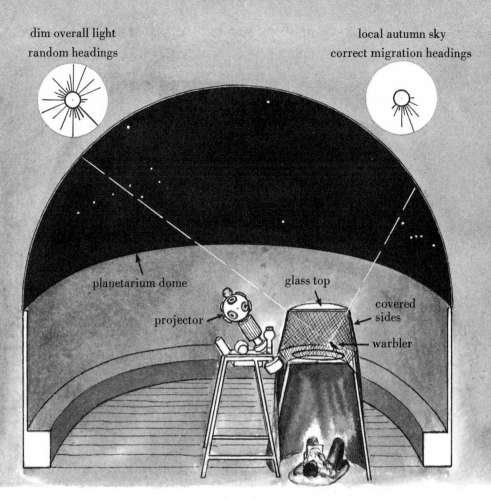

dim overall light
random headings

local autumn sky
correct migration headings

planetarium dome

glass top

projector

covered sides

warbler

Sauer's star-compass experiments

lighted the dome with a dim overall glow, so that it resembled a starless sky on an overcast night, the warblers showed only random, scattered headings. This finding agreed with an earlier one of Kramer. On cloudy days, when the sun was completely hidden, Kramer's starlings

137

had also wandered. Without the sun or stars for a guide, apparently both day and night migrants lost their bearings.

The cues of the night sky are very different from the single disc of the sun arching across the sky by day. At night a complex pattern of stars moves across the sky, rotating around the fixed point of the North Star. The question remained whether night migrants use the stationary North Star or an overall pattern of moving stars for their guide. To find out, Stephen Emlen, an American scientist, recently studied captive indigo buntings during their night migration periods in Michigan. Emlen used simple, inexpensive orientation cages that allowed him to test a number of birds at the same time. Each cage consisted of a two-quart metal pan, with an ink pad inside, and a funnel rolled from blotting paper stuck into it. The funnel was topped by a wire screen and cardboard extended above it to shut off the bird's view of any local landmarks. The standing bunting inked its feet, then hopped up to footprint the blotting paper again and again during its flight fidgets. The pattern of one night's footprints could be used to find the bird's headings, for the darkest part showed the main direction it pointed in during the night.

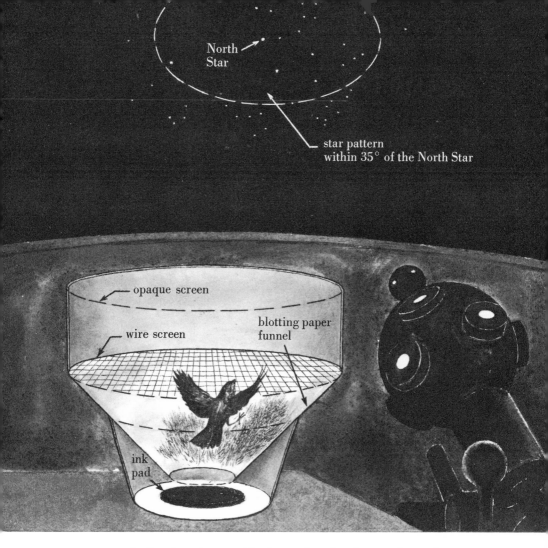

North
Star

star pattern
within 35° of the North Star

opaque screen

wire screen

blotting paper
funnel

ink
pad

Indigo buntings guide themselves by the northern sky.

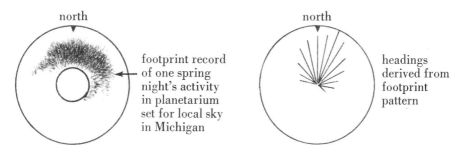

north

footprint record
of one spring
night's activity
in planetarium
set for local sky
in Michigan

north

headings
derived from
footprint
pattern

Emlen found that the buntings took northward headings in spring and southward in autumn. He then placed the birds under a planetarium sky and artificially shifted the star pattern. For example, he put the birds into the planetarium just after dark and showed them a sky they normally would see just before dawn. Still, the buntings kept heading on course. Evidently they were not allowing for star motion at different times of night.

To find out if the birds might be using single points in the night sky, Emlen switched off, one by one, on the planetarium projector, the North Star, the Big Dipper, the Milky Way, and so on. Blacking out any one of these landmarks, or even the entire southern portion of the sky, had little effect on the buntings' orientation. However, when the area of sky within thirty-five degrees of the North Star was turned off, the birds lost their bearings and headed at random. Emlen concluded that the buntings were using an overall pattern of stars around the North Star as a fixed guide for their compass headings. Further study will show if other night migrants also use this kind of star compass.

Scientists now generally agree that birds use the sun compass by day and the star compass by night. Recently, however, radar studies made over several years on night migrants in Illinois by Frank Bellrose and his co-workers have showed that birds do not have to see the stars by night in order to select and maintain their intended course. Bellrose reported that although the greatest number of migrants traveled under clear starry skies, large numbers of birds flew under heavy overcast with nothing visible overhead except thick dark clouds. By comparing their flight tracks on radar with the direction of winds aloft, he found that when the wind changed direction, the birds quickly changed their headings, adjusting their flight paths to allow for the effect of wind drift. Despite marked

Radar flight tracks of night migrants remain steady despite cloud cover.

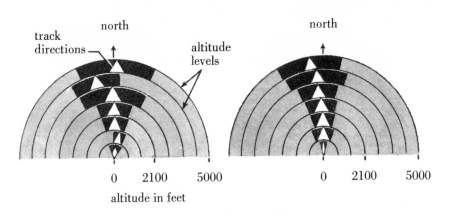

clear sky in spring   overcast the next night

Bird heads along
course set earlier
from sun or stars.

Sensing tail wind
blowing from left,
bird heads left
and flaps more easily.

Sensing head wind
blowing from right,
bird heads right
and flaps harder.

*how migrants might use the wind
to maintain course despite overcast skies*

shifts in wind direction, they could hold their course to within a few compass degrees.

Bellrose suggested that they might be using the wind itself for orientation. For instance, if a bird felt an increase in head-wind speed and a shift in wind direction toward its right side, it could flap harder to overcome the higher wind speed and turn slightly toward the right to allow for the drifting effect. By constantly checking any changes in the wind as they fly, birds may be able to follow a course through the night even under heavy overcast.

However, wind direction changes during the migration period, so birds cannot rely upon it as a constant cue for compass heading, the way they use the sun or stars. The answer may be that they use the wind as a check upon a flight direction already established by the sun or stars. Kramer had discovered that several species of night migrants are able to orient by the sun compass during the day. While watching one of his starlings during a period of cloudy weather lasting several days, he noticed that the bird was able to get its bearings quickly when the sun came out for two hours one afternoon. The next morning the sky was overcast once again, so Kramer expected to see the bird taking random headings. Instead, the starling was completely oriented, heading on its proper course. Thus, birds somehow may be able to record and remember their previous headings based on the sun and stars, then set out and maintain the proper flight direction, possibly by wind compass, even though the original cues have disappeared.

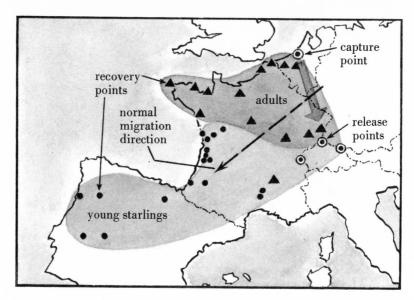

Transported young starlings flew by directional sense while adults used goal orientation.

Still compass orientation, using sun, stars, or any other means, does not fully explain how birds find their way. One experiment made this point clearly. Eleven thousand migrating starlings, banded in Holland, were carried southeast in the fall and released in Switzerland. These birds nest around the Baltic Sea and normally winter in Holland, Belgium, northwest France, and southern England. After they were released in Switzerland, band recoveries showed that most of the adult starlings did not fly in the usual southwest direction, but changed course and traveled northwest to reach their winter quarters. The young birds, on the other hand, relied solely upon a southwest compass direction and ended up in southern France and Spain instead of their regular winter homes. Clearly young and adult starlings were using two different types of orientation. The young birds were flying by an inherited compass sense, so strong that they were not influenced by the behavior of the adults. The adults, on the other hand, were able to allow for the wide shift from their normal range and to fly a completely new course.

Other species also demonstrate an ability to navigate by means other than search patterns for landmarks or any kind of compass orientation. Two Manx shearwaters, which breed on the tiny island of Skolkholm, off the English coast of Wales, were taken from their nesting burrows and released near Boston. One of the birds made its way back across the Atlantic Ocean to Skolkholm in twelve and a half days. It flew 3050 miles at an average speed of 244 miles per day.

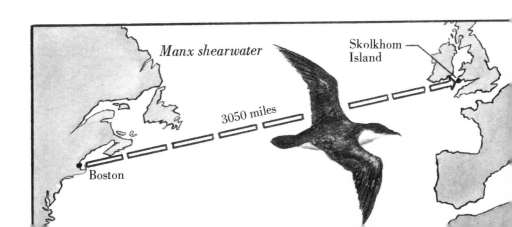

Manx shearwater

Skolkhom Island

3050 miles

Boston

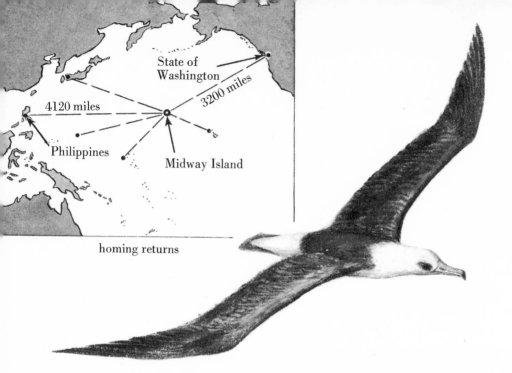

State of
Washington

3200 miles

4120 miles

Philippines

Midway Island

homing returns

Laysan albatross

Another example is the Laysan albatross, a smaller relative of the wandering albatross. Laysans have been released far from their nesting ground on Midway Island in the Pacific Ocean. One of them returned to Midway from the Philippine Islands, a distance of 4120 miles, in 32 days. Another bird, released on the opposite side of the Pacific in the State of Washington, returned 3200 miles to its nest in a little over 10 days. Returns at such high speeds indicate that these birds are determining their geographic position in unknown territory and setting their course toward a distant goal in a much more refined and complex manner. They seem to be finding their way by using goal orientation.

A human navigator can find his way with great accuracy by celestial navigation, using heavenly bodies as reference points to fix his exact position. Before Kramer and Sauer showed that birds use the sun and stars for compass orientation, the mere suggestion that birds might also use celestial navigation would have seemed laughable. Yet with this new knowledge scientists began to consider this possibility.

Geoffrey Matthews, an English ornithologist, worked out a theory that suggested how day migrants might navigate by the sun. Any bird, according to Matthews, is familiar with the particular arc the sun describes across the sky in its breeding and wintering territories. Finding itself in strange territory and wishing to return home, the bird might track the sun along a very short portion of its arc. It then might extend this short arc to construct the complete arc, including the zenith, or high point. Next it would compare the new sun arc with the familiar one from its home area to establish its location.

The angular height of the sun arc at a particular time of year is a direct indication of the north-south location, or latitude, of the observer. At the times of migration, during the spring and the fall, the steeper it is, the closer to the equator he is, and the more directly overhead the sun is at noon. If the new arc angle is too steep, the bird may be able to tell that it is too far south. If it is too shallow, the bird may realize that it is too far north. Thus, the bird would know which way to fly to correct its north-south position.

In addition, the bird may be able to use the new-found zenith point to tell if it is east or west of its home. The sun always reaches the zenith at noon at a point due south in the northern hemisphere. By comparing the new position at noon with the home position at noon, the bird can tell if the sun appears to be east or west of its familiar position. If the sun appears to be too far to the east, the bird must then move more to the east, increasing the angle between itself and the sun and placing the sun farther to the west of it. The reverse, of course, would also be true.

The new arc pictured in the illustration is steeper than the home arc, so the bird is too far south. Also, the new zenith is east of the home zenith, so the bird is too far west. Therefore, to reach home, the bird must fly north and east. This sun-arc theory provides a possible explanation of how a bird might find its north-south and east-west position, which would be true goal orientation.

148

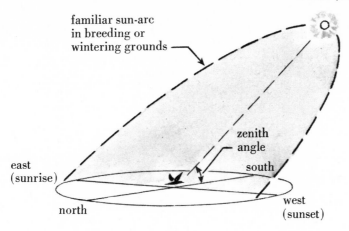

zenith (noon)

familiar sun-arc
in breeding or
wintering grounds

zenith
angle

east
(sunrise)

south

north

west
(sunset)

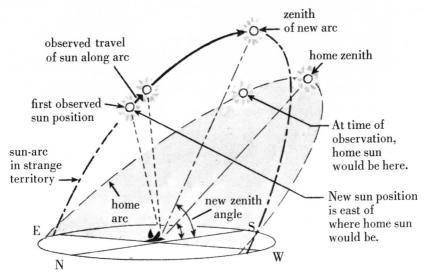

zenith
of new arc

observed travel
of sun along arc

home zenith

first observed
sun position

At time of
observation,
home sun
would be here.

sun-arc
in strange
territory

New sun position
is east of
where home sun
would be.

home
arc

new zenith
angle

E

S

N

W

Bird compares familiar sun-arc with sun-arc in strange territory.

Matthew's sun-arc theory

However, there are reasons why at least some birds are probably unable to use the sun arc in navigation. Recently, Helmut Adler, an American scientist, studied the inner clock of captive starlings in laboratory experiments. He found that they have a daily error of at least fifteen to twenty minutes. This time error makes any celestial navigation far too inaccurate to be useful. Nevertheless, although sun-arc navigation now seems impossible for starlings, other species may have developed finer vision and a more accurate inner time sense, allowing them to make the fast, precise sightings of the sun necessary for celestial navigation. Scientists are now studying the possibility that certain night migrants may navigate by tracking the motions of star patterns, a method that would seem to require even greater precision than the sun arc.

Perhaps scientists will find that there is no single answer to the question of how migrant birds find their way. Each species has certain unique life habits—feeding, courtship, nesting, flight, and so on—and their methods of travel may show just as much variety. Robins may rely on landmark and sun-compass orientation, because they need no other techniques to travel between their nesting and wintering grounds. Albatrosses and other species that must reach tiny mid-ocean islands on time may be able to navigate by the sun and stars as well as any human navigator. While traveling, migrants may be able to switch from one kind of orientation to another. If the sky is clear, they may use the sun or stars. If it clouds over, wind may be the cue they follow. If they fly over familiar terrain, land-marks may suffice. Birds have been migrating for many thousands of years, and they probably are flexible enough to take advantage of anything that will help them get from here to there.

The subject of bird migration is as vast as the distances the birds travel and as open to discovery as it was ages ago when man first noticed their comings and goings. Sci-entists have found some partial answers, but they have also raised many new questions that will require years of work to answer. Laboratory testing, airplane tracking, radar observations, banding, field study of migrant be-havior—all these and other means will be used to search for more knowledge on the travels of birds.

But you need not be a scientist to enjoy the great spectacle of migration. Everywhere around you, spring and summer, fall and winter, birds are on the move. In May the migrants pass in such numbers that an observer can sight dozens of species between dawn and dark. In

151

July, when most birds are at their nests, the shorebirds begin to whistle on high, as they head along their ancient pathways to the South. By November, when the autumn flights have passed, hawks, owls, and ducks arrive to spend the winter.

Experience is not needed to make a start observing bird migration. Binoculars can be bought at reasonable prices. Bird clubs, with experienced, helpful members, are located everywhere. If you would rather observe on your own, books are available for many regions, giving the times and places to look for different species. Make a list of the species you have seen, including the date, the location, the weather, and any other information that seems important. By keeping the list from one year to the next, you will get a good idea of the birds moving through your area. Once you start to notice the ever-changing activity of migration, a new world will open up to you. In this world countless birds, riding the wind, journey millions of miles over land and sea, using the sun, the stars, and the ceaseless motion of their wings.

Bibliography

(P) *means paperback*

Carr, Archie, *Guideposts of Animal Navigation*. Boulder: Biological Sciences Curriculum Study, University of Colorado, 1962. (P)
A short lively work on migration of different creatures, by a scientist who has experimented with sea turtles.

Dorst, Jean, *The Migration of Birds*. Boston: Houghton Mifflin Co., 1962.
The definitive work for the serious student. Migrations around the world and laboratory experiments treated in detail.

Griffin, Donald R., *Bird Migration*. Garden City, New York: Anchor Books, Doubleday & Co., 1964. (P)
An inside account by a scientist known for his work on orientation.

Peterson, Roger Tory, *The Birds*. New York: Time-Life, Inc., 1967.
Very readable. Contains much information related to migration.

Bibliography

Robbins, Chandler S., Bertel Bruun, and Herbert S. Zim, *Birds of North America.* New York: Golden Press, 1966. (P)
A field guide valuable for its migration maps.

Selsam, Millicent E., *How Animals Tell Time.* New York: William Morrow & Co., 1967.
A clear and thorough introduction to biological clocks.

Welty, Joel Carl, *The Life of Birds.* New York: Alfred A. Knopf, 1963.
An all-around study of birds with an excellent chapter on migration.

Index

About the author–illustrator

Born in New York City, John Kaufmann was educated at Brooklyn Technical High School, and the Pennsylvania Academy of Fine Arts. Later he studied and traveled extensively for a year in Europe. He now lives in Fresh Meadows, New York, with his wife and two sons, spending his summers in Maine. An established illustrator with a strong interest in nature writing for children, Mr. Kaufmann recently has been specializing in the study of bird migration, a subject involving his long interest in birds and flight.